ESSENTIAL

G000047971

Essential Russian Mythology

STORIES THAT CHANGE THE WORLD

PYOTR SIMONOV

Thorsons
An Imprint of HarperCollins*Publishers*

Τῷ φίλῳ Δημητρίῳ
ἀγάπης καὶ τιμῆς ἕνεκεν

Thorsons
An Imprint of HarperCollins*Publishers*
77–85 Fulham Palace Road
Hammersmith, London W6 8JB
1160 Battery Street
San Francisco, California 94111–1213

First published by Thorsons 1997

1 3 5 7 9 10 8 6 4 2

© Pyotr Simonov

Pyotr Simonov asserts the moral right to
be identified as the author of this work

A catalogue record for this book
is available from the British Library

ISBN 1 85538 475 2

Printed and bound in Great Britain by
Caledonian International Book Manufaturing Ltd, Glasgow

Contents

Introduction

Russian mythology, in the commonly understood sense of traditional, ancient narrative surviving in reliable literary transmissions, simply does not exist. We know very little about the remote religious past of the various Slavonic peoples. What is certain is that they spoke the same language and worshipped a number of gods; but this polytheism was more a complex body of heterogeneous beliefs than a unified, dogmatic mythological system. Moreover, this religion lacked the protective support of any social organization and thus yielded almost without a struggle to the official Christianity imposed upon the people by the will of the Kievan princes. Nevertheless, the passive resistance of the old beliefs was tough and tenacious; for while the old religion was forbidden from the close of the tenth century, when the new faith was introduced, ancient beliefs could not be so easily eradicated.

At first, it was only the city people who took Christianity more or less seriously. In remote rural districts, the old faith held its ground for a long time beneath the thin veneer of Christian rites. Indeed, Church historians are correct in describing Russian medieval religion as a 'dual faith'. People may have worn crosses and attended Orthodox Church services but they did not altogether abandon the celebration of earlier festivals. Gradually, the two rituals merged, with the Christian side gaining dominance, at least in outward appearance. Some historians even date the true conversion of the lower classes of the Russian people to as late as the fifteenth century. But exact dating has no meaning because even in the nineteenth century archaic survivals were still deeply rooted.

Consequently, the sources for our understanding of Russia's ancient beliefs and customs are those epic poems, folk tales, chronicles and biographical texts that offer reminiscences of a pre-Christian religion. Russian mythology is a special case: its features are revealed by derivation, deduction and more than a little divination. Those responsible for informing us about it did not have the subject as their *raison d'être* or intention for writing. Typically, early references to aboriginal religious beliefs are incidental remarks made by individuals in lengthy works on an entirely different subject. But thanks to their industry in preserving cultural traditions, we are able to piece together a remarkable and fascinating picture of the elements that made up the ancient Russian religious mind.

FOREWORD

Gods, Rites and Oral Tradition

Many centuries ago, nomadic tribes, heading west from the expansive Asiatic reaches and south from the verdant uplands where the Danube carves a frontier in northern Europe, settled in the Baltic and south Russian lands. Together, these people made up the first Slavs. The rich and colourful mythology that they developed was largely determined by the features of the physical geography that surrounded them.

Those who dwelt in the steppes were agriculturalists, tilling and cultivating the ground; they depended on the elements for their survival, on 'Moist Mother Earth' for their nourishment and for the nourishment of their cattle. In the south, by the banks of the Dniepr River, these people established their capital at Kiev. The Slavs of the north, surrounded by dense, rich forests and living along the shores of the Baltic Sea, were hunters, fishers and merchants who shared their lives with the eagle, the falcon and the wolf. Their capital was at Novgorod on the Volkhov River.

To these ancient Russians everything seemed alive; nature was a vital elemental force. Looking up at the hemisphere of the sky, adorned by day with the white clouds moving, and by night with the bright stars glowing, they came to think that supernatural beings governed not only the movements of these elements, but ultimately each person's own destiny. In time, stories and legends about the sun, the moon, the winds, the lightning, thunder and rain were told and retold, handed down from one generation to another and from one clan to another over hundreds of years. In this way the ancient Slavs came to believe in many gods and supernatural forces.

With the coming of Christianity, the veneration of the old gods, particularly Perun, Volos and Mokosh, was transferred to Biblical characters and to the martyrs and heroes of the new faith. Furthermore, the ancient deities, with their emblems, symbols and characteristics, were used to embellish the efficacy and spiritual valour of the Church's outstanding representatives.

For example, the prophet Elijah, who rode in a fiery chariot across the expanse of the heavens, assumed the function and personality of the powerful Perun, the old god of thunder and lightning. In many regions Russian peasants imagined that Saint Ilya (Elijah) struck the earth with lightning bolts from on high as he pursued demonic forces. At the prophet's feast on 20 July, bulls were slaughtered by the Russians to the accompaniment of sacred songs and blessings. The meat was prepared entirely by men and then taken to the Church where it was divided among the villagers. Perun/Ilya survived in the epic tales and legends as the mighty hero Ilya of Murom, who also rode on horseback above the still forests, just below the damp clouds, shooting across the sky and bringing bandits to justice. His marvellous arrows were capable of felling church cupolas and splitting robust oaks into thin slivers.

A second example is the holy shepherd, priest and martyr Saint Vlasii (or Blaise) who duplicated the name and duties of Volos, god of cattle and flocks, patron of commerce and merchants (*see below, pp.* 14–15). Saint Vlasii is honoured as the heavenly guardian of livestock and domestic animals. Many icons of Vlasii show him seated on a horse or on a stone, surrounded by cows, sheep and horses. The sacred images are found in stables or hung around the neck of each animal. In springtime, when the farm beasts are driven out to pasture, special prayers are said. The saying 'Those who honour Vlasii will always be in plenty' points to his ancient role as god of commerce and wealth.

Among the heroines of the church there is Saint Paraskeva, the third-century virgin martyr who underwent a considerable meta-morphosis in popular Russian veneration. She replaces an ancient Slavonic goddess, protectress of women and women's work, and of the fertility of the land. The date of her feast, 28 October, fell precisely within the marriage season and the period of women's autumnal work, particularly spinning. The connection of Paraskeva with the earth and fertility means that she can also be identified as a reincarnation of the goddess Mokosh, the great mother of plenty, and 'Moist Mother Earth' whose festival was also in autumn, after the harvest and at the beginning of the season of winter work.

Paraskeva's hair is long and always hangs loosely. In carnival processions, her icon is adorned with flax and birch branches.

Stories and legends of epic proportions were spun at the rich banquets of the princely courts in Kiev. In particular, it is around Prince Vladimir, the tenth-century Christianizer of Russia, and his valiant knights, that much of this epic lore concerns itself, much as the legends of the Round Table are grouped around the person of King Arthur. Like King Arthur, Prince Vladimir is rarely the prin-cipal figure of these tales, although he is known as the 'Bright' or 'Fair' Sun about whom the other planets revolve. Entertainers and minstrels sang of bygone heroism: of Ilya of Murom, who defeated an entire army single-handedly, and Dobrynya the Dragon Slayer (*see* Dobrynya Nikitich and the Dragon, *p.* 151).

Mythical beings were also brought to life in the homes of the northern peasants where, during the long winter months, ancient tales and sayings were solemnly recounted around the hearth by the old folk: tales of wood sprites, river nymphs and house gob-lins. Even in church, the brave feats and heroic adventures of holy men and women heard in sermons and readings were strongly reminiscent of ancient knights and fearless saviours of antiquity. In every genre there was reflected a strong feeling of cosmic life, of a primeval covenant between human passions and aspirations and the surrounding natural order.

Fundamental to Slavonic mythology is a primeval dualism which stems from the antagonism between creative light and destructive darkness. References are made to a white god of day and of light, opposed to a black god of night and of shadows: good against evil, the natural forces against the unnatural. Against this background, divine, human, animal and vegetable actors dramatize the eternal destinies of life and death.

Holy Russia

An uncommonly passionate attention was paid by the old Russians to phenomena that immediately affected their personal and tribal life – to events on, and more particularly *in* the physical earth. Eschewing an exclusive devotion to celestial forces, they concentrated a significant part of their spiritual dedication to the earth, to her power and sanctity, and to the mysteries that the earth sustains. Earth here must be understood in the very specific sense as soil, as a grain-producing farmland, as the pasture that is fertilized by the rain, pierced by the plough and turned by the hoe. Earth for the Russians is a mother: a moist, deep, dark, secret womb, the wellspring of all fecundity, the sustaining breast of nature, the final homeland of all humanity. It is the earth that nourishes; the earth whose inexhaustible energy spends itself and is mysteriously renewed year by year; the earth which sustains humanity, and in which at the end all come to rest. Fertility, rather than beauty, is the supreme virtue of Mother Earth, the eternal woman who at once embraces life and death: procreator, not virgin; pregnant, not chaste; a black welcoming cavity for the departed. She is both womb and tomb, nurturing human beings during their life, and then providing them with eternal rest. For these reasons, 'Mother Earth' lies at the core of ancient Russian religion. In her the most secret and deep religious feelings of the Slavs converge, and as the embodiment of kindness and mercy she reappears in a number of guises in folk tale and hagiography.

The Rite of the Earth

In times of drought, bad weather or danger, Mother Earth could be invoked by ceremonies and prayers to restore seasonable weather, to provide a rich harvest, or to eliminate the forces of gloom. The ancient Russians would arrive in the fields in the early morning carrying flasks of hemp oil. An elder would turn towards the east and pray, 'Moist Mother Earth, subdue every evil and unclean power so that no spell may be cast upon us or no harm come to us.' At the same time, the people poured some of the oil on the ground. Then, turning towards the west, he would say, 'Moist Mother Earth, engulf the unclean beings in your boiling pits, in your scorching flames.' Turning to the south, he continued, 'Moist Mother Earth, calm the southerly winds and all foul weather; pacify the drifting sands and whirlwinds.' And finally, facing the north, he pronounced these words, 'Moist Mother Earth, allay the north winds and the clouds, subdue the snowstorms and the cold.' At each petition oil was poured out and, when emptied, the flasks would be smashed on the ground.

It was said that Mother Earth could predict the future but spoke in an enigmatic language that only few could comprehend. Certain gifted sages would make a hole in the soil and close their right ear in it in order to listen to Mother Earth's mysterious language. As the breeze rustled through the grasses the Great Mother whispered her message. If the sage heard a sound that reminded him of a well-filled sleigh gliding over the snow, this was a sure sign of a bountiful crop. But if the sound was that of an empty sleigh, the harvest would be poor.

Mother Earth would also punish the proud, as illustrated in the symbolic story of Svyatogor, a huge and powerful giant whose boast that he could lift the earth led to his death (*Svyatogor, Mother Earth and Destiny*, p. 132). Thus, Moist Mother Earth, mystical and maternal, is the only source of life and strength who defines the limits of human experience. She is sacred but hers is an objective sanctity, for through her the entire vast, awesome territory of Russia declares a unique message and assumes a divine purpose. In Mother Earth we see the origin of the concept 'Holy Russia' and the belief in her destiny to enlighten and to sanctify the world. This belief is based essentially on an exalted understanding of relationships: among people, between humanity and the created universe, and between humanity and the divine. The glorious history of the Russian people reflects a holy purpose, one that demands noble deeds, wise leaders and faithful followers. Moist Mother Earth, as cradle and coffin of Russia's heroes, constitutes the fertile and powerful landscape in which symbolic acts of life and death are played out in dramatic ritual.

Death and the Clan

Intimately associated with the honour paid to Moist Mother Earth, and the belief in the powers of nature, was the cult of the dead coupled with the respect given to kinship ties. Each Russian clan constituted a social entity made up of members both living and deceased. The latter were particularly venerated and their assistance was sought in time of need. Special homage was paid to the original founder of a clan and in pre-Christian times all the dead became minor gods, with the chief ancestor assigned as the house patron or house spirit.

Moist Mother Earth becomes clearer to us in the light of ancestral worship and clan consciousness. The mystery of eternal birth and death is common to both; for just as the seed, buried in the damp earth's womb, gives new life to the ear of corn, which is procreated through the death of the seed itself, so is a child brought into life from the seed of his parents to form a link in the endless existence of the clan. From the parents we come and to the parents we return, into the womb of Moist Mother Earth. During earthly existence, Russian values were determined by the elders, by the will of the living and by the traditions of the departed. The Russian was not a child of heaven, but the fatherless son of the Great Mother, Mother Russia herself, who taught mercy and fidelity to blood relatives and, by extension, to all humanity. It is important to appreciate these features of ancient Russian religion, for together they form the deepest stratum of Slavonic religious beliefs.

After death it was believed that the soul had to embark upon a long journey. According to one idea, it was obliged to sail across a wide sea, and therefore coins intended for the spirit's passage-money were placed in every grave. In later times there existed the custom of burning or burying the dead in boats or boat-shaped coffins. Another tradition explained that the journey had to be made on foot, so a corpse was sometimes provided with a pair of boots, intended to be worn during the pilgrimage and discarded at its termination. The destination was the 'other world', which could either be located in the rainbow or in the Milky Way. A third view of the soul's wanderings was that it had to climb a steep hillside, sometimes supposed to be made of iron, sometimes of glass, and at its summit was situated the celestial land of eternal goodness.

Special burial sites underlined a strong belief in life after death. In addition to food offerings made at the cemeteries, everything deemed necessary for the afterlife – weapons, tools, clothing, wives, slaves, horses and hunting dogs – was buried in the grave or was burned if the deceased was cremated. The corpse itself was robed richly and was seated next to his consort who voluntarily chose death (usually by stabbing) in order to enter the afterworld with her husband. A funeral banquet was consumed and the ceremonies continued for several days and nights.

The Slavonic Pantheon

Owing to the paucity and ambiguity of the relevant sources, our knowledge of the ancient Slavonic gods is far from adequate. As indicated above in the Introduction, ancient Russian religion does not represent a unified or structured system of beliefs but rather a complex body of heterogeneous traditions. Unlike the Baltic Slavs, the eastern Russians neither built temples nor used the services of a regular class of priests. Their sacrifices were offered up under a tree (generally an oak) or beside running water, and the sacred rites were performed by the elders, or heads of family communities, who exercized the functions of priest, king and judge.

Nevertheless, in spite of the scantiness and vagueness of our knowledge, it is valuable to assemble what information exists to see the way the functions, properties and epithets of the gods are inherited by the figures in sagas, epics, traditional lore and hagiography.

The Gods of the Eastern Slavs

The old Russian capital Kiev was regarded as the home of the gods, so these are sometimes referred to as the 'Kievan' pantheon.

Perun

Perun is the chief deity of the ancient Slavonic pantheon. He was mighty, widely venerated and greatly feared; a god of thunder, lightning, storm, violence and war. He is acknowledged as fertilizing the land with the spoils of battle by bringing to it bounty and riches. Through cloud cover and lightning he inseminates rain-moistened Mother Earth during the violent passion of the thunderstorm. His sacred symbol, the oak tree, was thought to attract lightning, and his weapon was the mace.

In his name, together with that of the god Volos, the Russians concluded peace treaties and ratified oaths with the Christian Byzantines.

When, in 944AD, mighty Prince Igor was concerned to negotiate a treaty of non-violence with the Byzantines, he summoned the envoys in the morning and led them to the hill where Perun's statue stood high. Laying aside their armour, shields and swords, Igor and those of his subjects who held to the old faith took a solemn oath before the god's image, while the Christian Russians did the same in the Church of the Prophet Ilya. Igor directed these words against those who would violate the pact: 'May they never receive aid either from God or from Perun; may they never have protection from their shields. May they be destroyed by their own swords, arrows and other weapons and may they be slaves throughout all time to come.'

Perun's home was 'on high': above the sky, on the mountain top or in the uppermost branches of a giant oak. These are the sacred locations he chooses for his annual epiphany. They were considered to be the centre of the earth, the navel from which it developed outward. From there he governed the elements: wind, rain, frost, drought, thunder, lightning and hail, commanding them to create havoc or make a rescue, depending on his mood. His mace, which became identified with the thunderbolt, had magic powers. Once thrown from on high at bad people or evil spirits, it returned in boomerang fashion to his hand. Perun's bolts were believed to pass through the earth, penetrate it to a particular depth, and after a certain time (usually seven years and forty days), gradually return to the surface in the form of oak trees or grain or even the long, black stones that were used to preserve the people and land from lightning and conflagrations.

In the spring, Perun could be seen going forth in his fiery chariot, crushing his enemies, whose wounds often stream with blood, with blazing arrows shot from the rainbow. Others have seen these flashes pierce the heavy spring clouds, causing them to send showers of rain to moisten Mother Earth. These flaming darts were often understood to be a golden key with which Perun unlocked the earth and released its concealed treasures, its restrained waters, its captive founts of light. With this key he also locked away in safety those who were pursued by malignant wizards. This is Perun's gilded lightning-key, with which in spring he pierces the clouds or splits the winter-bound earth and lets loose the frozen streams.

The spring rains have always been looked upon as not only health-giving but also life-giving, and accordingly there arose the myth of the water of life, a precious beverage which on many occasions restores the dead hero to life. This liquid may be carried by the elemental messengers of Perun: the Whirlwind, the Thunder, or the Hail. It may also be carried by their 'types': the Raven, the Hawk, the Eagle and the Dove. In many stories, two species of water are brought; one is called 'the water of life', the other 'the water of death'. When the water of death is applied to the wounds of a corpse it heals them; but before the dead body can be brought to life, it is necessary to sprinkle it with the water of life, after which the corpse first shudders, then sits up, and usually remarks, 'How long have I been asleep?' (See *Prince Ivan, the Firebird and the Grey Wolf*, p.74, and *Ivan and Ivan, the Soldier's Sons*, p.104). In deep winter, it is actually Perun himself who dies and who remains lying veiled in a fog-like shroud, floating over the dark waters in a coffin of cloud until the spring showers recall him to life. At that time he, or his messenger birds, recover gems and treasures which evil spirits have hidden away within mountains or under deep waters. In so doing, the lights of heaven are brought out from behind the dark veil of winter.

As the god of cloud and thunder, Perun is often represented either as a bellowing bull who rages and makes a horrible noise or as a virile he-goat. In either form, he sheds the fertile seed, the generative spring showers, that moisten Mother Earth and make her fecund. He is thus the husband of Mother Earth, whose purifying thunderbolts exorcise the evil winter spirits, herald the spring and strike the bride who wakes from her barren, winter sleep. To him or to his emblem, the giant oak tree, the Russians would sacrifice live cocks, animals such as the bull, bear and he-goat, and humans. They then pegged arrows around the tree.

Some traditions present Perun as a tall and vigorous man, with black hair and a long golden beard. Riding in a flaming chariot drawn by a he-goat, he clutches in one hand his mace, or a quiver full of arrows, and in the other a fiery bow. He disperses evil people or spirits and can arouse mighty storms. Perun often appears as a beneficent deity, humane and just, the overseer of right and order, although also very restless and extremely impatient. He does not suffer liars, thieves, the proud or the selfish. Not only does he punish the wicked but he also hunts demons, whom he smites with his lightning.

Khors

Khors is one of the sun gods in the Kievan pantheon on whom the people relied for good harvests and seasonable weather. Sun worship is at the core of the old Slavonic religion and it expresses the essence of the ancient Slavs' world philosophy. The concepts of light, of fire, and of the generating forces of man are associated with the sun. The name Khors is the old Russian word for the 'sun' itself. As a god, he symbolizes absolute Good as contrasted with Evil and he plays an important role in the prehistoric notion of the original, all-embracing, creative force that reveals itself through different emanations.

This affinity between the sun, light and goodness continues into Christian thought. In a famous legendary dialogue between Prince Vladimir and King David, the former asks the following two questions: 'How did the White Light originate? Where did the Sun come from?' King David answers: 'The White Light originated in God's heart; the Sun from God's face.'

The concept of the Radiant Sun is often expressed in terms of the sun's 'crown'. Some old Russian tales declare that the sun is wearing the tsar's crown and that Tsar Sun rules over twelve kingdoms (the twelve months or the signs of the zodiac); or that the tsar resides in the solar disc and his children in the stars. All these children are bathed, tended and serenaded by the sun's celestial maidens.

The northern Slavs charted the course of the sun in order to predict the fortunes of mankind. One of their temples, situated on a high mountain, was so built that it was possible, through special apertures in its dome, to observe the first points of sunrise and sunset. Precious stones were inserted in various parts of the shrine and magic solar signs were carved in stone. Special prayers were addressed to the east at dawn, and by coordinating the data on the course of the sun, and the magic meaning of the precious stones and of the signs, Slavonic mystics prophesied future events. For example, at an eclipse, when it was said that the sun had been devoured by wolves, the mystics forewarned terrible disasters, such as earthquakes, the outbreak of war, fire, famine or plague. It was customary for the dead to be buried with their heads to the east, or with their eyes or face oriented eastward.

Svarog

Svarog is the divine tsar of the sky, occupying the highest place in the Slavonic pantheon. He is the supreme deity, the all-powerful god of the heavens who is sovereign over the entire universe and over the other gods. Sunlight and Fire are his divine offspring; they proceed from his blood; the former under the name of Dazhbog, and the latter under that of Svarozhich. Svarog is concerned only with the cosmos, to his offspring he deputizes the work of creation and the task of ruling over the earth. In the primeval struggle between the forces of Good and the forces of Evil, Svarog is the shining hero who stirs up a whirlwind by fighting the hideous serpent.

As the personification of the sky and as the creator of Sunlight and Fire, Svarog is at one moment illumined by the sun's rays, at another enveloped in the dark storm clouds and made brilliant with lightning. In the shadows of these clouds he would kindle the flame of the thunderbolt and produce celestial fire. As for earthly fire, Svarog sent it as a divine gift to earth in the form of lightning. By splitting the clouds with flashing arrows, Svarog would cause the sun to appear; he would ignite the torch of the sun which had been extinguished by the demons of the shadows and the morning sun would emerge from the veils of night. The concept of regeneration was connected with the sunrise and the renewal of its flame. Svarog was thus a divinity who gave light to the sun and fire to the celestial and earthly hearth.

Svarog is also the divine smith, the master craftsman associated with fire and generative power who hammered the sun into shape and placed it in the sky. Furthermore, he perfected the art of forging weapons and had the ability to transform himself into a whirlwind, a falcon, a gold-horned aurochs,[1] a boar or a horse.

Dazhbog

Dazhbog is the son of Svarog and is occasionally identified as a sun god. His name means 'giver of wealth' and his functions appear to have been concerned with the creative and economic aspects of the sun (light, life and the bountiful harvest), rather than the cosmic. As the divinity of the day and of heavenly light he conquers the shadows, cold and misery. In epic songs the Russian people are referred to as 'the grandchildren of Dazhbog'.

Every morning Dazhbog rides out in his radiant chariot from his golden place in the east, in a land of eternal summer and abundance, to cross the celestial vault. This resplendent two-wheeled carriage is encrusted with diamonds and is drawn either by twelve white fire-breathing horses with golden manes, or by three horses, one gold, one silver, and one diamond. He begins each journey as a handsome youth, reaches maturity at midday, and dies in the evening as an old man. Similarly, Dazhbog ages

---

1.   A wild European bison (or buffalo) – now extinct.

gradually in the course of the year and at each morning or each new year the cycle of life and death begins afresh. He is attended by two beautiful maidens (the morning and evening stars), seven judges (the planets), and seven messengers (the comets).

Dazhbog's marriage to Lada, the goddess of the spring (*see Dazhbog and Lada p.*29), secured the promise of bounty and abundance in the world.

Svarozhich

Svarozhich is the son of Svarog, and the god of solar and earthly fire. As patron of heat and warmth, Svarozhich empowers the newborn winter sun. For this reason he is sometimes portrayed as a warrior, dressed in armour and always accompanied by a horse. His helmet resembles a bird with outstretched wings and on his breastplate is the head of a black bison which symbolizes his power. In his right hand he holds a shield and the left grasps a double-edged axe. At harvest time, Svarozhich kindles the fire over which the ears of corn and sheaves of wheat are laid to dry before the threshing.

Stribog

Stribog is an elemental god of the air, cold and frost whose grandsons were the Winds whom he commanded. He is occasionally called the 'distributor' or 'apportioner' of wealth.

Volos

Volos is the god of cattle and flocks, patron of commerce and merchants, divine protector of poetry and oracles and tsar of the underworld. His grandson was the singer and poet Boyan. The Russians ratified oaths with foreign treaties in his name, along with that of Perun. In certain myths he is seen as the opponent of Perun in the cosmic struggle between the celestial deity of the elements, here the thunder god Perun who lives in high places (*see p.* 9), and the noxious viper Volos who lurks below (at the base of the world tree, beneath stone, in his earthy kingdom), in order to control the horned beasts. The thunder god pursues his opponent, striking him either in the tree or under the stone with his flaming arrows, burning or fracturing him. Perun is victorious and the sign of his victory is the appearance of heavenly water, the rain which moistens the earth. The serpent Volos is forced to dwell forever in earthly waters. Sacrifices of cocks and human infants were made to certain stretches of water in which Volos was known to reside.

As described above, pp.2–3, Volos's Christian representative is the shepherd and martyr, Saint Vlasii, who continues to be the guardian of cattle and domestic animals.

Iarilo

Iarilo is the son of Dazhbog and Lada and god of ardent love, fecundity, spring germination and regeneration. He is strong and handsome, the courageous protector of the fields, who, barefoot, rides a white horse and dresses in a white cloak with a coronet of wild flowers on his brow. In his left hand he holds a sheaf of rye and in his right a human skull. At the command of his mother, Lada, he opens the gates of the sky and charges earthward: an advent that marks the beginning of spring. This takes place at the vernal equinox which signifies the approaching spring thaw, a time when the sun's potency rapidly rises and the forces of procreation awaken. Towards the end of the summer he returns to the heavens. An ancient song tells of Iarilo: 'Where he treads with his feet, there is abundance of rye; And where he casts his eyes, ears of wheat will spring.'

Simargl

Simargl is a winged griffin or divine Bird-Dog that guards the sacred tree which supplies the seed for every plant. Simargl is also the name of the magic Firebird who helps heroes and protects home and family (*see* Prince Ivan, *the Firebird and the Grey Wolf, p.* 62).

Mokosh

Mokosh is the only female deity in the Kievan pantheon and is possibly the name of the Russians' great earth goddess. Especially venerated by women, her name means 'moist'; it suggests her unity with the waters of the skies and of the earth. Indeed she is frequently associated with sacred wells and streams and is known to have life-giving powers. During the winter, in vain Mokosh roams the pastureland of the earth in order to fructify the soil, but it remains desolate and barren. Bedewed by Perun and purified by his lightning flashes, she lies in the dark and cold recesses of earth where she is discovered by the comely Iarilo. He woos her with his ardent sunbeams and adorns her with oceans, seas, rivers, lakes, grass, trees and flowers. As his wife, Mokosh loves Iarilo and bears him an endless number of children that populate the sky, sea and land: birds, animals, fish, insects and, finally, humanity.

Mokosh is the protectress of women, the goddess of fertility, childbirth and all the animal world. She is represented as having long hands and a large head and at night she shears sheep or spins and plaits flax. As a life-bestowing and death-granting fate goddess, Mokosh spins the thread of existence and dispenses the water of life that revives nature after its winter sleep.

Mokosh is the only ancient deity whose name survives from old Kievan times into Russian folklore, as late as the early twentieth century. (See Ivan Savelevich and the Rusalka, p.33.) In later Christian times, her metamorphosis is into the saintly Paraskeva who is the patroness of spinning, health, marriage and fertility (see above, p.3).

Another transformation of this goddess of death and regeneration is Baba Yaga (see Vasilisa the Beautiful and Baba Yaga, p. 53). Although normally depicted as an evil old hag who steals and eats children, persecutes the hero and threatens him with death, Baba Yaga also has another, more maternal and sympathetic side that shows her links with Mokosh. Occasionally, Baba Yaga is revealed as a kind, wise, prophetic old woman who befriends the hero or heroine, offers magical objects or processes needed to accomplish tasks (such as passage through her initiatory hut), provides nourishment and gives true direction to a longed-for destination. With her mortar and pestle she performs her dual functions of fertilization and destruction of enemies.

Distinctly female, Baba Yaga has, at the same time, a definite male counterpart in folk legends, Koshchei the Deathless, who is either Baba Yaga's son or nephew. He possesses the power of flight, is able to hang from a single hair, and can endure fire without being burned. The epithet 'Deathless' refers to his cycle of dying and rising. In stories, his soul is held in an egg in the womb of a duck hidden in a secret place. If this egg is found and cracked, it releases his soul and Koshchei falls dead, only to revive through the water of life. (*See Koshchei the Deathless, p.*42.)

The Gods of the Baltic Slavs

Sventovit

Unlike eastern Russians, the Baltic Slavs possessed a priestly class and built substantial temples to their gods, usually in places of difficult access and often surrounded by fortifications. Their supreme god, the four-headed Sventovit, was connected with light, bounty, fertility, war and clairvoyance. His centre of worship was in Arkona, on the island of Rügen where there was a famous citadel built at the edge of a rocky promontory that was washed by the sea on three sides.

At the cliff's summit, in the middle of the town, and near a major source of water, stood an impressive rectangular temple built of wood. This was richly decorated with embossed ornaments and multi-coloured wood carving, and the whole was covered by a red roof. Inside the stronghold was a barbican, whose four pillars stood free of the outer walls of the temple and adjoined some of the carved beams of the roof. Heavy embroidered curtains hung from the four pillars, forming an enclosed space: an inner sanctuary within which rose a gigantic statue of Sventovit, over eight metres high. Other idols also accompanied him; all were made of wood, often decorated with metal or costly stones and provided with various objects, such as armour, helmets, swords and goblets.

Sventovit's four heads and necks were joined together and faced north, south, east and west. The faces were beardless and the hair cut short. The right hand of the statue held a drinking horn inlaid with various metals which, for purposes of divination, was annually filled with mead by the high priest; the left hand was set akimbo. Sventovit wore a close-fitting mantle and near his feet on the temple floor lay the god's bridle, his saddle, and an enormous sword whose blade and scabbard were richly chased and damascened with silver. He was a fearsome warrior god who had a large appetite for human sacrifices, and the treasury in Sventovit's sanctuary was regularly replenished by a portion of the spoils of war: gold and silver goblets, huge bull's horns encrusted with precious stones, gold-plated weapons, saddles and banners. A sacred war banner was also kept in Sventovit's temple. Before setting off for battle, the priests would display it to the god's private army of 300 horsemen.

A beautiful white horse with prophetic powers, consecrated to Sventovit, was venerated by the people of Rügen as an incarnation of the god himself. No one was permitted to touch it other than the priest. It was believed that Sventovit mounted on this charger and waged war against those who defied him; and in the morning the steed was often found bathed in sweat after having been ridden through the night. Success or failure in war was divined in a special ritual involving this horse. The detachment of soldiers would not embark upon a military expedition or a sea voyage unless it indicated favourable omens three times in succession. In front of the temple the priests would arrange three rows of spears; in each row the spears were grouped in pairs with the spearheads pointing downwards. After uttering a solemn prayer, the priest took the white horse by the bridle and led it over the spears. Should Sventovit's horse step over the first row with its right foot first, this was taken as a favourable omen, the future augured well and the mission would be undertaken. But if the order was reversed, this presaged disaster: no action was taken and the enterprise was abandoned.

Because Sventovit's predictions always turned out to be true, he became highly renowned for his victories, riches and prophetic powers. All the northern and western Slavs honoured him as the god of gods. Compared with him, the other deities were mere demi-gods who must be obedient to him. Tributes and gifts were sent to him from many neighbouring lands; kings and princes sought his prophecies and his favour. Even a captive Christian was chosen by lot every year to be sacrificed to him.

During the annual harvest festival the god would predict the following year's crop. At the harvest, a great feast was held in honour of Sventovit at Arkona. The people assembled from all quarters of the island to sacrifice cattle in front of the temple and to participate in the oracular rites. At the forefeast,[2] the inner chamber was meticulously swept and cleaned by the high priest who alone had access to it. While he carried out his duties inside, he was very careful not to breathe; and when he could no longer hold his breath, he hastened to the door lest the presence of the deity be desecrated by the air expelled by a mortal man. The next day, while the people waited anxiously outside, the priest made a careful inspection of the quantity of mead that remained from the previous year in the drinking horn held in the right hand of Sventovit's statue. If the beverage had diminished over the year, a poor harvest was predicted for the next, and the people were advised to preserve some grain for the ensuing drought. If the opposite were the case, the priest foretold abundant crops in the following year.

2. The forefeast was the day before the feast or festival; for example, 24 December is the forefeast of Christmas.

Thereafter, having poured the mead out at the feet of the statue as a libation, the priest refilled the vessel and drank a toast to the god, beseeching him in solemn words to bestow upon himself and his country all the good things of this earth, such as victory in war and an increase in prosperity. When the prayer was finished, he emptied the goblet in one draught, and replenishing it with mead, he put it back in the right hand of the idol.

At the end of this ceremony, a round, honey-flavoured festal cake, the size of a man, was brought into the temple and placed between the priest and the people. The priest then asked them whether or not he was still visible behind the cake and if the people answered affirmatively, he expressed the wish that next year the cake would conceal him completely. If granted, this wish would ensure them a better harvest and an increase of crops for the coming season, since it would mean that the cake would be proportionately larger still, so as to hide the whole of the priest's body and thus make him quite invisible. Finally, the priest admonished the Rügians to do dutiful homage to Sventovit and urged them to remain constant in their faith. This would secure them victory on land and at sea. At the ritual meal that followed the sacrificed animals were consumed by those present. It was considered a religious obligation and a proof of piety for one to eat and drink to excess on this occasion.

Triglav

Triglav was a many-headed deity of the north-western Slavs whose worship was centred in Stettin, Pomerania. There his image stood in a temple located on the highest of the town's three hills. The statue was made of gold but its three heads, joined one to the other, were entirely silver-plated, the eyes and lips being covered with a golden veil. Triglav's priests declared that the three heads stood for the three realms over which the sovereignty of the god extended, namely, the sky, the earth and the underworld, while the veil was meant to prevent the god from seeing the sins of men and from speaking to them. He was referred to as the 'greatest of all gods' and thus may have been a manifestation of three major gods or three aspects of a single god.

His temple was richly sculptured both inside and out and used as a storehouse for war booty. On its interior and exterior surfaces were embossed numerous figures of men, birds and animals, so lifelike that many people believed that they lived and breathed. Their colours always looked new and seemed resistant; neither moisture nor the winter frost could damage them. Following an ancient custom, one-tenth of all the spoils of battle was held in the treasury of the temple. Owing to the warriors' frequent victories there was always an abundance of gold and silver vessels, daggers, knives and other costly objects, which were used by the leaders on festive occasions. Furthermore, enormous horns of wild bulls, gilded and encrusted with precious stones, were kept in the treasury. Some served as drinking vessels and others as musical instruments.

A noble black horse was consecrated to Triglav and played an important part in his worship. Like Sventovit's sacred horse, no man was permitted to mount it, and it was used in divinations. In the forecourt of the temple, whenever a warlike expedition was about to be undertaken, the high priest placed nine spears, in three rows of three, about a metre apart. He then led the black horse, now decked with a gold and silver saddle, three times across these spears. If it stepped over them without touching any, it was considered a favourable omen and the expedition was embarked upon. This use of a black horse in addition to his connection with the underworld indicate that Triglav stood in opposition to Sventovit, the god of heavenly light, who rode on a white horse.

Minor Deities

Aside from the high gods of the preceding pantheon, the Slavs also honoured other beings of a lesser order who were credited with supernatural powers. These included nymphs, sprites, imps, dryads, elves and goblins that inhabited trees, forests, stretches of water, the sky, the celestial bodies, the storm, the home, the hearth and fields. Sacrifices of fruit, birds and poultry were made to all these and divinations were sought. Belief in these spirits was part of the general veneration of the forces of nature. The regular return of the four seasons was understood as so many changes in the struggle between sun and frost, resulting in the yearly revival and death of vegetation as well as the death and reproduction of animals and men. Moreover, the honour paid to the elements was also adapted to the cycle of labours in both agricultural and cattle breeding, and from this earth-oriented belief-system there evolved what may be called an 'agricultural religion' of the ancient Slavonic people, with its natural symbolism and periodic festivals.

Ancient Russian religion was contingent on an agrarian population. It was emphatically a religion of the tillers of the soil. The life of the ancient Slav revolved around the house, the yard, the stable, the forest, the field and the river, and the most important religious ideas and emotions were therefore connected with these essential elements in their daily life. Each of these elements was imagined to possess a soul, and this soul acquired anthropomorphic features and an independent existence. In this way arose the conception of a demon population that either helped or hindered man's relationship with nature.

Many traces of this religion have been preserved in folklore, and following Russia's conversion to Christianity the old festivities and personalities were adapted to, or merged with, the celebrations and divinities of the new faith. A popular legend tells that when Satan and all his host were expelled from heaven, some of the exiled spirits fell into the lowest recesses of the underworld, where they remained in the shape of goblins. Some, however, were received by the woods which they haunted; others dived into the rivers and streams; some remained in the air and delighted in riding the whirlwind and directing the storm; and some attached themselves to the houses of mortals as domestic spirits. Many of these, through their association with humans, became benevolent.

In addition to the reverence paid to the forces of nature, there was at the same time a lively cult of the dead, for in pre-Christian times all the departed became members of a lower pantheon whose veneration represented a cardinal element in Slavonic religion. The male deity Rod, whose name actually means 'kin', is often linked to the notion of a dying and reviving vegetation god, or to the general power of birth and reproduction inherent in each clan. Many believed that Rod, sitting in the air, cast mounds on the earth in which children were born. The Rozhanitsy are female deities, linked with Mokosh; they watch over the birth of children and animals, ensure the fertility of the land, and control individual destiny. In their honour, meatless feasts were prepared and offerings were made of bread, porridge, curd and mead. Their following was essentially private and domestic.

Earlier, the importance had been noted of the vital relationship between kinship and ancestral worship, and it was the deified Rod and Rozhanitsy who symbolically embodied the collective souls of the dead ancestors in Mother Earth. Thus the cult of the dead was intimately intertwined with the cult of nature.

Domovoi

The dead are potent enough to assist or endanger the living, according to the former's character or to the latter's ritual zeal. The chief of the ancestors, or the founder of the clan, is revered as a particular patron of the house who is called by the general name of *Domovoi* ('house-spirit' or brownie), essentially a later transformation of Rod. (*See The Domovoi and the Two Peasants, p.*30.)

Rusalkas

Unhappy maidens who met a premature or violent death were turned into nymphs called rusalkas and dwelt in the river depths or at the bottom of lakes. These deaths may have occurred through drowning, strangulation, suicide, perhaps before baptism or other initiation ceremonies. Clan consciousness would have forbidden proper ritual burials and so the spirits of these lonely girls, as they were considered unclean, were deprived of the necessary preconditions for the welfare of their souls.

Rusalkas are often glamorous young women with fair, transparent skin and long, loose, green or golden hair that they comb sitting by the side of a river. However the northern Russians saw the rusalkas as ugly and shrewish beings with dishevelled hair and violent tempers. It was felt best to treat them with kindness and pity so modest gifts, such as wreaths of flowers, were brought to the riverside to appease them. Legends from the north tell of youths who were beguiled by the magic powers of these wanton sprites and tried to marry them, and live a normal human life with them. Inevitably, such attempts proved fruitless and always ended in tragedy. (See *Ivan Savelevich and the Rusalka*, *p*.33.)

The male counterparts of the rusalkas were known as vodyanoi; malevolent, dangerous water sprites that inhabited lakes, pools, streams and rivers and who demanded drowned men as tribute. They had a variety of appearances: some had a human face, paws instead of hands, outlandish big toes, long horns, a tail and eyes like burning coals; others resembled tree trunks gliding across the surface of the water aided by translucent fairy wings; yet others were aged men with green beards that turned to white with the waning of the moon and then back to green again at the new moon. Although they were immortal, their age was governed by the phases of the moon, growing now younger, now older.

Leshiis

In certain parts of Russia trees were held to be the residing place of the souls of the departed. Trees marked a sacred zone and, as a living organism, were on an equal footing with human beings. The spirit of the soul that inhabited a tree could, if need be, relocate to another tree and this led to the notion of various wood spirits or demons, known as leshiis.

Every October the leshiis disappeared or died until the following year. In spring they were especially wild and dangerous, roaming the woods which they guarded, whistling, shouting with rage and punishing men by leading them around in circles – making them blunder helplessly in all directions through the undergrowth, only to lead them back to the spot where they had begun. But as they were generally good-natured, their victims were usually released unharmed. It helped a lot if the victim knew how to escape the leshii's spells. One foolproof way was for the victim to sit under a tree trunk (preferably that of an oak), take off all his clothes and put them on again backwards. An important detail, never to be neglected, was that he must put his left shoe on his right foot, and vice versa. (*See The Farmer and the Leshii, p.37, The Tailor and the Leshii, p.39*).

The Tradition of Storytelling in Russia

Irrespective of genre – myth, legend, folk tale or epic song – the stories preserved from Old Russia have all been learned by ear and handed down through oral transmission from father to son and from mother to daughter for generations. Indeed, it was not until the seventeenth and eighteenth centuries that the earliest attempts were made to commit them to writing. Meanwhile, even before Prince Vladimir established his capital at Kiev, the art of storytelling had been created, developed and cultivated by people from all classes of Russian society: peasants, hunters, farmers, workers, soldiers, vagabonds, sailors and peddlers. By the tenth and eleventh centuries the tradition of storytelling was at its fruition and it continued to occupy a prime position in the communication and transmission of beliefs, values and traditions for nearly a thousand years.

This became a refined art involving talented and responsible tellers with phenomenal memories and the ability to recreate the tales afresh with each recitation, but without altering their essential elements. Almost without exception the narrators were totally illiterate. They were, however, steeped in a tradition that provided them with a thesaurus of motives, anecdotes, riddles, proverbs and formulas, which they would skilfully weave into the age-old tales. The stories were told and retold whenever and wherever individuals came together: in taverns, around the hearth, by camp fires or in one another's homes.

The themes of these stories have much in common with the mythology of the theological traditions of other countries: destiny, life and death, the quest for a Utopia, the recovery of paradise lost. Invariably, obstacles must be overcome, remedies obtained and supernatural assistance sought. Furthermore, conflict is at the heart of most of the plots: a king in need of assistance or medicine; a fabulous creature that creates havoc; a country ravaged by a monster; a wicked stepmother. The hero or heroine must be prepared to undergo trials and anxieties before accomplishing a task, and the difficulties encountered are usually proportional to the honour and bliss finally achieved.

The element of the mysterious or the miraculous is fundamental to the success of a venture. In the Russian stories the magical and the mundane exist side by side. Activities like working, eating, sleeping, riding a horse and marrying are interconnected with supernatural acts or powers that influence the physical world and alter the normal cosmic order. Habitually, the sense of other-worldliness is evoked by formulaic phrases such as the following typical opening: 'In a certain village, neither far from here nor near, neither high nor low...' or with the imponderable phrase: 'beyond the thrice-nine lands to the thrice-tenth kingdom', where the extraordinary can be achieved so long as the hero behaves in a prescribed fashion. Often a task will be successfully accomplished only after it has been undertaken three times: three princesses to be liberated, three battles to be waged, or three brothers setting off in search of a life-saving object. A ferocious dragon may have twelve tails or heads to be severed; or seven days, months or years may have to pass before adverse circumstances turn favourable. The recurrence of events suggests ritualized action and the repetition of words and phrases ('Moist Mother Earth', 'turbulent head'[3]), indicates the litanical language of ceremony and belief. Proverbs and slogans like 'the morning is wiser than the evening' have a significant place in the vocabulary of the tale teller. Even the natural environment participates in the magical, mysterious order. The tree, especially the ubiquitous 'damp oak', identifies a sacred zone and symbolizes strength and life, since it nourishes the atmosphere above it and is itself nourished by the moist earth below.

The epic tales constitute a special category of their own. They are anonymous, rhythmic narratives about the great exploits of national heroes, either historical or mythical. Formerly, the stories were chanted, by heart, to what we today would view as rather monotonous tunes that were confined to a limited number of notes and conventional musical phrases. They could also go on for a very long time. The texts ranged from between one hundred to eleven hundred lines of poetical prose. In Russian they are called *bylinas*, from *byt*, 'to be', meaning that the tales were of something which actually took place and not simply accounts of a purely imaginary event. For both the singers and their audience believed implicitly in the existence of the knights and heroes they celebrated.

The earliest of bylinas predate the reign of Vladimir and tell of fabulous champions and giants richly endowed with superhuman qualities. These are the 'Older Heroes': Volga, Mikula and

3. As well as referring to the physical head and the myriad thoughts that whirl around in it, this phrase also means 'one's very self', or 'whole being'.

Svyatogor, the debris of ancient Slavonic mythology whose adventures, through generations of retelling, are dislocated from prehistory and brought forward to the Vladimirian epoch. The second and largest cycle is concerned with the adventures of Prince Vladimir's knights in and around Kiev. Aside from Vladimir himself, the poems extol the heroic personalities in his retinue, some of whom may be historical characters, including Ilya of Murom, Dobrynya Nikitich and Alyosha Popovich.

A third cycle relates to heroes of a different political milieu – the citizens of the wealthy trading city-state of Novgorod – 'My Lord Novgorod the Great', as it was commonly styled by her inhabitants. This smaller collection boasts two important heroes: Sadko the rich merchant and Vasili Buslayevich. The tales paint a lively picture of the wealth and activity of Novgorod at the height of her prosperity and their resemblance to medieval metrical romances places them in contrast to the heroic narratives of the Kievan epics. In these tales the protagonists are not always lauded but are portrayed semi-satirically. Even the Church is not exempted from caricature. The treatment of Vasili and his adventures is in a light-hearted tone, while his godfather the monk appears wearing the bell of the cathedral of Saint Sophia as a helmet, and using the clapper as a walking stick (*see Vasili Buslayevich the Brave of Novgorod, p.*174–5).

Taken as a whole, the entire corpus of orally transmitted Russian narratives presents a buoyant mix – older practices and beliefs are intermingled with Christian piety. Abounding in magic and fantasy, the tales, songs and stories run the gamut from gods and giants to folklore and historical truths. The material shows us that the Russians were clearly not romantics; but they respected nature, were faithful to their clan, saw in suffering an element of sanctity, and fought for truth. Since many of the qualities are much in evidence even today, we must surely see in these stories the primordial and essential features of Russian traditions and values.

1

Remnants of the Old Gods

Dazhbog and Lada

The sea god, Tsar Mora, had nine beautiful daughters who lived in grottoes in the blue-green depths of the sea. His favourite child of all was Lada. She was fair of face and her tresses were long and golden. Every day she would row on the sea and out to the ocean in a golden boat with silver oars. The great whales and dancing porpoises kept her company and listened in wonder to the mysterious, captivating songs that welled up from the depths of her soul.

One day, Dazhbog the sun god was crossing the heavens in his gleaming chariot drawn by twelve fire-breathing horses with golden manes. As he passed, he leaned out to gaze upon the lovely siren whose sad notes had reached his ears. Lada looked up and playfully splashed some water at him, and immediately the sun god fell deeply in love with her. He descended on a sunbeam to the seashore and called for Tsar Mora, imploring him to allow his daughter to join him in the Golden Palace of the East. The sea god became angry: 'Give up my precious daughter – Lada? It's unthinkable!' He ordered his giant sea horses to thrash and trample upon Dazhbog until he fell senseless under their feet.

But Dazhbog's father, the divine tsar of the sky, Savrog the all-powerful god, heard the cries of his child, and caused a black cloud to blot out the rays of the sun. In the darkness, Dazhbog was able to escape from the power of Tsar Mora, but he resolved to win Lada despite her father's opposition to the marriage.

Together with his faithful brother, Svarozhich the fire god, who knew the weaknesses of women, Dazhbog devised a plan. Along the seashore they spread out a collection of glamorous dresses and a pair of wonderful green slippers. Then they hid behind a nearby oak tree. The young goddess saw these lovely things from her boat, and they so took her fancy that she rowed quickly to the shore to admire and to take them. As her boat touched the sand Svarozhich leaped out, snatched her away, and carried her to his brother. When he learned of this, Tsar Mora raged with fury. He raised up mighty storms whose waves smashed angrily against the cliffs. But Lada was never to return to her watery home. She married Dazhbog and because of her radiant beauty she was given charge of the spring, the season of light, life and growth. In due time she bore Dazhbog a son, who was named Iarilo.

The Domovoi and the Two Peasants

Every dwelling was believed to have its own house-spirit who was thought of as an old dwarf either living under the threshold, in the stove, or in the horse stall. The stove, in particular, was the most important item in the house. Even when a clan moved house it was customary to carry live ashes from the old fire to kindle the new one. In this way the spirit of the ancestors remained with the clan to guard and to provide for them.

When the master of the house was required to set out on a long journey, great care was taken to ensure that the house-spirit, or domovoi, would not leave with him. One precaution taken was to make sure that the lid of the stove was securely fastened and that the grate door was bolted shut.

The domovoi's body, though of human shape, was very hairy; silky fur covered him even to the palms of his hands. Occasionally domovoi were seen with horns and a tail, or as an old man wearing a fur coat, or they may even have had the aspect of an ordinary bundle of hay. Their chief business was to care for the cattle herds and protect the entire home and its occupants from misfortune. When a farmer acquired a new animal he would introduce it diplomatically to the domovoi by leading it around the yard, asking if its colour was suitable and saying he hoped that the spirit would make the new arrival welcome. The domovoi were particularly partial to horses; they would feed them at night with sugar cubes, comb, groom and plait their tails and manes. Although the domovoi could be spotted by the living, it was difficult and dangerous to do this as they disliked being seen and punished people for their curiosity, as well as for their neglect of them. It is important to remember that the domovoi, like all the dead, needed to be fed and treated with respect. If not given due honour, the domovoi might abandon the home, and his departure would result in illness, great misfortune, or the death of householder or cattle.

Once there were two peasant farmers who lived in a village not far from Kazan. One owned three healthy, spirited, silky-skinned stallions who worked energetically and never seemed to tire. The owner was very pleased with and proud of these stallions because due to their industry he made a good profit and could provide all the necessities of life for his family. The other farmer also had three horses, but these were weak, lazy and without lustre. As a result, this farmer made great losses and his family were always hungry and in want. Naturally, he was very jealous of his neighbour and sought to find out the secret behind his well-fed steeds.

'I don't know,' said the more fortunate peasant. 'It almost looks as if the animals are being secretly fed in the night – but I know nothing about it!'

So one evening both of them kept watch, hidden behind an enormous oak tree. For a long while there was nothing to see. But at midnight, as they crouched behind the oak tree, they spied a very strange-looking, dark and bearded dwarf approach the horses. The moon shone brightly and the farmers could see the stranger quite clearly petting, grooming and even whispering to the horses. Then he filled their trough with water and gave all the horses a drink before vanishing from sight.

The following morning, the peasant who owned the horses noticed that the trough was still full of water. So was the barrel from which the family drew water to drink. His envious neighbour realized that it must be the stranger's magic water which was bringing health and strength to the horses and prosperity to the family. He was determined to spoil his neighbour's good fortune.

'This domovoi is up to no good,' he craftily told his neighbour. 'His water may benefit your animals but I know that it is harmful to humans. The wicked spirit has charmed it and will bring you much suffering.'

Stupidly, the peasant believed him. 'What shall I do?' he asked.

'The poor fool trusts me,' thought the cunning neighbour, 'I'll be able to make his life miserable!' Aloud he said, 'I suggest you drill a hole in the barrel. You can plug it up during the day, but at night remove the stopper so that the magic water drains away.'

The next evening the domovoi tried to fill the barrel after the horses had had their fill. When he saw the magic water escaping through the hole, he was outraged at the peasant's distrust of him. Screaming with fury, he vented his temper on the farmer's horses, kicking and beating them. Not satisfied with this, he set fire to the barn and stables and finally killed all the cattle and horses.

When the peasant saw what had happened he cried out to the domovoi to forgive him and to restore his farm, but it was too late. Because of his own foolishness, and lack of respect and gratitude, he had found disfavour in the eyes of his domovoi and nothing ever prospered with him again.

Ivan Savelevich and the Rusalka

Unhappy maidens who met a premature or violent death were turned into nymphs called rusalkas and spent their lives in the river depths or at the bottom of lakes. They were mistresses of the waters, often glamorous young women with fair, transparent skin and long, loose, green or golden hair that they combed sitting by the side of a river. Gazing into its waters, they saw their reflection and admired their beauty. With their magic combs, the rusalkas were able to produce water at any time so they could survive with safety for long periods on dry land. At the beginning of summer, they came out of their underwater crystal palaces, climbed trees and danced about in wild abandon, causing the grass and grain to grow in abundance. On clear moonlit nights they promenaded and sang, made coronets of flowers or swung on the boughs of trees overhanging the rivers and lakes. Always naked, they were often seen with fishtails and were able to turn themselves into fish, toads and frogs.

However, the rusalkas were frequently lonely and forlorn and in search of companions with whom to share their lives. A favourite trick was to bewitch passers-by with their beauty and their sweet voices. Children would be tempted by their alluring gifts: baskets of fruit and nuts, sweet pastries and biscuits. Like sirens, they lay in wait for the imprudent in order to overpower them with their charms. Men, especially, were enticed off forest paths or lured into their wild dancing and then would be tickled to death, or dragged into the rivers where they drowned, or became the rusalka's slaves. They lived in crystal palaces, ornamented with gold and silver which came from sunken vessels, and lit by a magic furnace that shone far brighter than the sun.

Ivan Savelevich was a seal hunter from the northern trading city of Arkhangelsk. One bleak and dark day, he was out in his boat on a hunting trip when he became stranded near a glacier in the Arctic Circle. He struggled to return home, but he was forced to spend the bitter winter on a windswept and barren island called Novaya Zemlya. The nights were very long and very lonely, but he kept up his spirits by singing, playing his balalaika, or repairing his small wooden hut. The only light he had was from the blazing hearth and his small table top lamp.

One evening he dozed off earlier than usual and lay sleeping on a rug near the stove. The fire in the fireplace had burnt itself out and the lamp glowed very dimly. A strange swishing sound woke him up with a start; but it stopped as quickly as it had started. Ivan was too anxious to sleep again, so there in the dark he picked up his balalaika and began to play a melancholy air in order to soothe his nerves. Once more the strange sound filled the room. This time it resembled the patter of dainty feet dancing. Terrified, Ivan kindled the fire in order to see who was making this noise. 'How could anyone have come here?' he thought. 'Could it be an evil demon?' But there was no one to be seen; the hut was totally empty.

Taking courage, Ivan extinguished the fire and the lamp to test his elusive guest. Picking up his instrument, he strummed a merry tune and, once again, he heard the rustle of playful footsteps in the room. He darted in all directions with outstretched hands pursuing the invisible dancer but all he succeeded in doing was to stumble over his chair and fall helplessly on the rug. The room was as empty as ever. Night after night the same thing occurred:

the sound of elf-like dancing to the strains of Ivan's balalaika, but never anyone in sight. Finally, Ivan set a better trap. He concealed four burning candles behind a heavy curtain so that the hut was still quite dark, but as soon as he started playing and heard the shifting feet moving in time to his music, he quickly drew the curtain aside and, behold, standing in front of him was a beautiful young maiden. She was fair and slender like a lily and her thick golden hair tumbled down to her ankles and covered her body.

'Who are you and why are you here?' asked Ivan, astonished at this sight.

'I am a rusalka,' the maiden told him. 'I live in the river near the town of Nizhnii Novgorod. In my former life as a human I died very young – a witch was jealous of me, and I pined away and died. My poor parents mourned my death for eighteen years. They pleaded with the goddess Mokosh to bring me back to them. At long last, the goddess granted their wish, so that during certain seasons I am allowed to live on land. But this can only happen so long as I am in the company of just one person. But now that I have seen you and danced to the music of your balalaika, I love you dearly and cannot live without you. Will you marry me?'

Ivan was totally captivated by the rusalka's beauty. He forgot that one day he would need to return to the company of other humans, and he agreed to be her husband.

Their first winter together was very happy indeed. The little wooden hut was made beautiful with a woman's touch and whatever they needed appeared as if by magic, thanks to the supernatural powers of the rusalka's comb. For Ivan the days flew by quickly and at night there was much music, dancing and merrymaking. Gone were his evenings of loneliness and sorrow.

With the coming of the spring thaw, however, Ivan knew that he had to return to Arkhangelsk to sell the hides that he had stored throughout the cold season. When she heard this, the rusalka cried bitterly and clung to Ivan.

'Do not go back to Arkhangelsk,' she implored him. 'Stay here with me, for I cannot live in the town and survive! In the depths of the sea, I have a beautiful mansion made entirely of crystal. Let us go there together. You cannot imagine what mysteries lie on the sea bed.'

But the thought of spending a lifetime underwater did not appeal to Ivan, and he insisted on leaving the rusalka for the town.

'One day you might wish to see me again,' the rusalka said to Ivan. 'I shall always wait for you. This is how you can find me. A short distance east of Nizhnii Novgorod there is a small stream that flows through a forest into the great Volga. At that junction you will find a very tall oak tree and beside it a deep pool. Either at high noon or at the stroke of midnight climb that oak and dive into the pool. There below I shall be waiting for you.'

With that they bid each other a tearful farewell.

In due course Ivan concluded his commerce and trade in Arkhangelsk. He visited all his old friends and acquaintances and enjoyed town life. But throughout the whole time he never forgot his lovely dancing rusalka. He longed for her greatly and eventually made up his mind to travel to Nizhnii Novgorod. Following the rusalka's directions, he located the stream, the forest and the giant oak tree beside the pitch black pool. Ivan peered searchingly into the pool's depths.

'Are you down there waiting for me, my love, my rusalka?' he wondered. 'Or is this a horrible trap? I am afraid of drowning, I am terrified that I might fall into a sea-monster's lair!'

Little wonder that he hesitated for so long; little wonder that he doubted the rusalka's promise. On that first day Ivan made no decision; he remained deep in thought amidst the protective branches of the tall oak. As dusk fell and the moon rose, Ivan picked up his balalaika and, without knowing why, gently stroked its taut strings. He produced a lilting melody whose modulations rang through the forest. In the glow of the moonbeams, sad Ivan caught sight of beckoning ripples on the pool's surface, small waves and circles ebbing and flowing in time to the music.

'My rusalka is dancing,' exclaimed Ivan. 'I must go to her now.'

It was one minute to twelve o'clock when Ivan made up his

mind, and exactly at midnight he plunged into the dark, mysterious pool. As his agile body penetrated the surface, the waters opened wide and then closed again over him. It was an embrace from which he would never be released. In a flash the pool was pacified, the waters flowed calmly and night descended on earth and on sea.

Deeper and deeper Ivan descended until he reached the river bed. It was dark and sepulchral and he feared the worst. But at last his rusalka bride appeared and embraced him. Ivan spent many happy months in the watery kingdom but eventually became homesick. He longed to be with other people and to feel dry land under his feet. But this was impossible. He could never go back. Having succumbed to the call of the water spirit, he was forever a prisoner of her love.

The Farmer and the Leshii

Leshiis were quixotic sprites who haunted the forests. They looked like shrivelled up old men who, because of the blue blood in their veins, had a bluish complexion in their cheeks. They had green eyes that often popped out of their sockets, tufted eyebrows, rough skin, long hair, a long green beard, and cast no shadow. The leshiis rarely kept themselves tidy; their shaggy, tangled hair covered them from the horns on their head to their cloven feet.

A leshii's stature was altogether unpredictable. Sometimes his head reached the tops of the tallest trees; at other times he could be the tiniest gnome and could hide himself under a leaf. They could also transform themselves into all kinds of forest animals and birds, especially the bear or the wolf who enjoyed their special protection. They would often steal infant children, especially the unattended and unbaptized.

Once, a leshii disguised as an itinerant pilgrim sought hospitality at a farmhouse in a remote part of the south Russian countryside, quite close to a thickly wooded forest. The farmer welcomed the traveller, fed him generously and put him up in a warm, cosy room for the night. After breakfast the following morning, the stranger offered money as payment for the lodging, but no matter how much he insisted the farmer refused.

However, seeing the pilgrim to be a wise and sober man, the farmer asked him for some advice. 'What must I do?' he complained. 'My farmland here is near a dense forest that is inhabited by wild beasts. Whenever my cattle stray into the surrounding woodland they easily get lost or become prey to the ferocious animals.'

'To repay your kindness,' replied the guest, 'I think I can offer some assistance that will be to your benefit. One of my helpers will come to lend a hand. What you must do is simply release your cattle from the farmyard enclosure each morning and you will see that in the evenings they will return to you totally unharmed. But you must remember one thing: once you have sent them out, make certain that you do not follow to see what becomes of them.'

The farmer hesitated to begin with. 'What a strange proposal,' he thought. 'How do I know that I won't lose my whole herd?' But eventually he took courage. 'Very well,' he said, 'I accept your offer, and I give you my word that I will abide by your conditions.'

And, to his relief, everything seemed to turn out most agreeably. For three years the farm animals wandered off in the morning, and in the evening returned of their own accord, unharmed. Moreover, they were well-fed and groomed; the cows' milk was never better. One day, however, the farmer's curiosity got the better of him.

'I must see for myself who is taking such care of my cattle!' he said to himself. An hour after the cattle's departure, he set off, followed their tracks, eventually to discover them grazing in a field. At a little distance was a bent and withered-looking old lady leaning heavily on her cane, her head bowed low. As if swaying to the tune of a lullaby, she rocked sleepily from side to side.

Wishing to make her more comfortable, the peasant removed his cloak and placed it flat on the grass. He took her by the arm and said, 'Babushka, please lie down and have a rest.' But the old lady ignored him, and even as he spoke, she continued to rock from side to side, her movements growing slower and slower until finally she became completely motionless. Then in the twinkling of an eye she disappeared. Dumbfounded, the farmer returned to his home. But the very next day, his cattle did not come back on their own. In fact, they were never to be seen again. The old woman, you see, had been the leshii's assistant and, by breaking his promise, the farmer had also broken the spell and paid the penalty.

The Tailor and the Leshii

In the city of Kazan there was once a young and talented itinerant tailor who went from place to place seeking employment. Many months had passed and because he had been totally unsuccessful at finding work, his own health and welfare were suffering. He was thin and ragged, and could not keep himself warm. One day, out of desperation, he cried, 'Even if a leshii himself were to ask me to sew something, I would do it.'

As soon as he had uttered these words, an elderly man came running towards him. 'Why are you so sad, my son?' enquired the old man. The tailor explained his sorry state, and the stranger said, 'Come to my house, for I have a sheepskin blanket that needs to be sewn up.' Delighted at this sudden change in fortune, the tailor gladly accepted the offer.

Together they walked quite some distance beyond the city limits and entered a verdant valley where the old man's house stood. He summoned his wife to come out and meet the tailor. When she heard that he was to sew a blanket, she offered the following words of advice: 'Make sure that you are not like the many other tailors who have passed through this house. None of them was capable of doing the job properly. There is only one way to make a success of it: when my husband brings you the sheepskins, take care that you do not remove or discard any of the end pieces, especially the feet.'

Eventually the old man produced an enormous stock of skins and the tailor set to work. Remembering the advice of the old woman, he spread them all out on the floor and stitched them together very shrewdly and resourcefully so that no end piece needed to be snipped away.

When the old man examined the finished product he was very well satisfied.

'Since you have done so well with the blanket,' he said, 'I want you to sew a sheepskin coat with matching hat and mittens for my little grandson.'

Once more the tailor set to work and, as before, he took care not to cut off any end pieces. Again, the finished articles met with the man's satisfaction and, as a result, he gave the tailor many more sewing jobs. However, after several months' work the tailor had still not been paid, so he approached the old woman to ask her when he would get some money.

'Have some patience,' she said. 'You have worked well; we have never known a better tailor. Very soon my husband will pay you. But mark you this: when he asks you for an accounting, do not demand a particular sum of money but rather say, "You yourself know what I have done and the quality and value of my work."'

As before, the tailor followed her advice and when the time came he replied exactly as he had been told to. Then the man went directly into his house and came out leading a beautiful and splendidly attired young damsel. 'For your excellent work I am offering you a wife,' he said to the surprised tailor, 'and with her comes a handsome dowry. You will receive a golden carriage with three fine horses as well as fifty roubles for your purse.'

As he spoke, three magnificent steeds adorned with silver bridles and a yoke on which were suspended a set of shiny spherical bells galloped up. Behind them was a most magnificent carriage.

Putting his bride into the vehicle and taking the reins himself, the tailor proudly rode back to Kazan and to the house of his mother and father whom he had not seen for three long years. Very soon arrangements were made for the wedding. Word soon spread about the good fortune of the tailor – his lovely bride, his fine horses and his wealth. Many of his friends came around to see the impressive animals.

'Wait a moment!' said someone. 'I recognize those horses. They used to belong to our village elder, but they were stolen several years ago. Thief! Thief!'

When the elder was brought to the house, he immediately recognized his magnificent horses and promptly accused the tailor of robbery. The tailor was totally lost for words.

'If only the old man who gave me the horses were here now!' he thought to himself. 'He could explain everything.'

In an instant the man was there, standing between him and the elder. 'So,' cried the leshii (for that indeed is what he was) to the elder, 'how is that you are clever enough to recognize your horses, but not your own daughter? You left her unguarded under the oak tree in the forest behind your house one morning twenty years ago! I stole her from her cradle and she has been with me ever since. This tailor whom you falsely accuse of theft is your future son-in-law!'

Reduced to tears, the elder, himself a well-to-do trader, led the young couple back to his house for a grand feast. He gave them a wedding fit for royalty and was forever grateful to the tailor for rescuing his precious daughter unharmed from the hands of the cunning leshii.

2

Folk Tales

Koshchei the Deathless

Long ago in a certain kingdom there lived a tsar who had an only son. When the prince was very little, his nurses and governesses sang lullabies to put him to sleep: 'Lu-la, lu-la, little Prince Ivan. You will grow up and wed a beautiful maiden for yourself. Beyond the thrice-nine lands in the thrice-tenth kingdom, in a tall tower dwells the Princess Vasilisa Kirbitievna whose marrow flows from bone to bone.'

When the prince reached his fifteenth year he asked the tsar's permission to go and seek his bride. 'Which way will you go?' the father asked. 'You are still too young.'

'Not at all, father. When I was young, my nurses and governesses sang me to sleep with lullabies and told me who my bride is and where she lives. Now I wish to go and find her.' The tsar reluctantly gave his blessing to the youth but first sent reports to kingdoms far and wide that his son, Prince Ivan, was setting out to find his bride.

Eventually the prince arrived in a certain town, gave in his horse for grooming, and took a walk through the streets. He soon came to a square where a man was being flogged with a whip.

'Why do you punish this man?' he asked.

'Because he owes a prominent merchant ten thousand roubles,' they answered, 'and he has not repaid his debt on the specified date. And, be warned, if any man decides to redeem him, that person's wife will be carried off by Koshchei the Deathless.'

The prince pondered this deeply and then departed. After walking about the town, he happened to return to the same square and found that the man was still being whipped. Prince Ivan took pity on him and decided to pay the ransom money. 'After all,' he reflected, 'as I have no wife, none can be taken from me.' He handed over the ten thousand roubles and then set off to his lodgings.

Suddenly the man who had been released ran after him, crying, 'Prince Ivan, thank you! If you had not paid my ransom, you would never have won your bride. Now it is my turn to help you. Buy me a horse and a saddle at once!'

Puzzled, the prince purchased a horse and a saddle and then asked the man his name.

'I am Bulat the Brave,' he replied.

The pair mounted their steeds and set forth on the road. They travelled beyond the thrice-nine lands, and eventually they reached the thrice-tenth kingdom. Bulat outlined his plan.

'First arrange for a good supply of chickens, ducks and geese to be bought and roasted, so that there will be plenty of everything. Meanwhile I shall go and bring you your bride. Just remember, every time I return to you, cut off the right wing from one of the birds and serve it to me on a plate.'

Bulat the Brave went directly to the high tower in which Vasilisa Kirbitievna was sitting. There he carefully threw up a pebble to attract her attention. Unfortunately, the pebble broke the gilded top of the tower. He ran to Prince Ivan and said to him: 'Why are you sleeping? Give me some chicken right away.'

The prince cut off the right wing of a chicken and presented it to Bulat on a plate. Seizing the food, Bulat raced back to the tower and called out, 'Good day, Vasilisa Kirbitievna! Prince Ivan sends you his greetings and has asked me to give you this chicken.'

The princess was considerably alarmed at these strange events, and remained speechless. But Bulat himself answered for her: 'Greetings, Bulat the Brave! Is Prince Ivan well? Thank God that is so. But why do you stand there, Bulat? Take this small key and open the cupboard, then pour out for yourself a glass of vodka, and God speed you.'

Then Bulat rushed back to Prince Ivan. 'Why are you sitting down?' he asked. 'Quickly, give me some duck.'

The prince cut off the right wing of a duck and presented it to Bulat on a plate. Seizing the food, Bulat raced back to the tower and called out: 'Good day, Vasilisa Kirbitievna! Prince Ivan sends you his greetings and has asked me to give you this duck.'

Vasilisa was speechless and taken aback, so Bulat himself answered for her: 'Greetings, Bulat the Brave! Is Prince Ivan well? Thank God that he be so. But why do you stand there, Bulat? Take this small key and open the cupboard, then pour out for yourself a glass of vodka, and God speed you.'

Then Bulat again hurried back to the prince. 'Why are you resting? Be quick and give me some goose.'

The prince cut off the right wing of a goose and presented it to Bulat on a plate. Seizing the food, Bulat hastened back to the tower and called out, 'Good day, Vasilisa Kirbitievna. Prince Ivan sends you his greetings and has asked me to give you this goose.'

This time when Bulat appeared with the strange gift, Vasilisa Kirbitievna immediately took a key, opened the cupboard and offered the stranger a glass of vodka. But instead of taking the glass, Bulat seized the maiden by her right arm and pulled her smartly out of the tower. He set her on a horse and galloped off at high speed. Bulat, the princess Vasilisa and Prince Ivan sped away into the distance.

The following morning, Vasilisa's father, Tsar Kirbit, learned to his dismay that not only had the top of his tower been broken but also that his daughter had been kidnapped. He raged with anger and immediately ordered pursuers to set out in all directions.

In the meantime, our knights errant and their captive maiden had ridden a long time or a short time when Bulat the Brave took off his signet ring and pretended that it was lost. He then said: 'By your leave, Prince Ivan, ride on and I shall turn back to look for my ring.'

But Vasilisa Kirbitievna began to implore him thus: 'Bulat the Brave, do not abandon us. Here, take my own signet ring instead.'

'That is entirely out of the question, Vasilisa Kirbitievna, for my ring is priceless. It belonged to my dear mother and when she gave it to me she said, "Wear it, lose it not, forget not your mother."'

Bulat the Brave retraced their steps at a gallop and soon met up with the tsar's guards pursuing them on the road. Immediately he slew all of them, except one who would bear the ill tidings to the tsar. Then he hastened to catch up with Prince Ivan and Vasilisa. They rode for a long time or a short time and then Bulat the Brave concealed his handkerchief and pretended that it was lost.

'Ah, Tsar Ivan. I have mislaid my handkerchief. Continue your journey and I shall catch up with you soon.' He turned back and after going several miles he met another band of pursuers, in fact twice as many as before. He killed them all and then returned to his companions.

'Have you found your handkerchief?' the prince asked.

'I have,' replied Bulat.

Night fell as they rode. They pitched a tent and Bulat lay down to sleep. Before retiring, he set Tsar Ivan to guard the tent, saying, 'If anything happens, be sure to wake me.' Hour after hour the prince stood to attention, but gradually his eyelids began to droop and drowsiness overcame him. Eventually he sank down by the tent and fell into a deep sleep. Suddenly, and without warning, Koshchei the Deathless appeared from on high and carried off Princess Vasilisa.

When at daybreak Prince Ivan awoke and found his bride gone, he wept bitterly. Bulat the Brave also woke up and asked the prince why he was weeping. 'How can I not weep, for someone has stolen Vasilisa Kirbitievna!'

'I warned you to stand on guard. This is surely the work of Koshchei the Deathless. Let us hunt him down.' They rode for a great many days until they came upon two shepherds watching their flocks. 'Whose flocks are these?' they enquired.

'They belong to Koshchei the Deathless,' answered the shepherds. Bulat the Brave and Prince Ivan continued to question the men and managed to discover how far Koshchei's home was from there, the way to find it, the hour that the shepherds usually returned with the flocks, and where the animals were penned for the night. Then Bulat the Brave and Prince Ivan dismounted and strangled the shepherds, put on the shepherds' clothes, and drove the flocks homewards. When they reached Koshchei's house, they went up to the gates and stood there.

Meanwhile, Vasilisa had not been treated cruelly in her captivity to the fearful Koshchei. He had presented her with a she-goat and she bathed herself each day and night in the goat's milk. On the day that Bulat and Prince Ivan arrived, they saw the servant girl come out to the pen and milk the goat as usual. Prince Ivan took out a gold signet ring which Vasilisa had given him and dropped it into the bowl of goat's milk that was being taken to her. The servant girl thought that the shepherds were playing silly pranks, so she went to the princess to complain.

'Those shepherds are ridiculing us,' she said. 'They have thrown a ring into your milk bowl.'

'Never mind; let them be,' replied Vasilisa. 'Bring the milk so I can strain it.' She strained it, saw the signet ring and at once called for the shepherds. Bulat and Ivan stepped forward.

'Good day, Vasilisa Kirbitievna!' said Bulat the Brave.

'Good day, Bulat the Brave! Greetings, Prince Ivan! How has God brought you here?'

'We have come for you, Vasilisa Kirbitievna. No matter where you were, we would have found you; even at the bottom of the sea.' The princess seated them at the table and fed them various meats to eat and wines to drink. Bulat made a special request: 'When Koshchei the Deathless comes back from hunting, ask him where his death is. And now it would not be a bad idea for us to conceal ourselves.'

The guests had no sooner gone into hiding than Koshchei the Deathless came flying back from the hunt. 'Faugh!' he exclaimed. 'Hitherto no Russian spirit has entered my domain; but now I smell the smell of a Russian and it offends my nose.'

'You are imagining things,' said Vasilisa gently. 'You have been flying over the Russian lands so long that you yourself are sated with its scent, and now you fancy it is here.'

Koshchei ate his dinner and lay down to rest. Vasilisa approached him, threw herself on his neck and caressed him fondly, saying, 'My dearest Koshchei, how I have missed you. I began to believe that my eyes would never gaze upon your face again. I feared that wild beasts may have devoured you.'

'Foolish woman,' he laughed. 'Your hair is long, but your wit is short. How could wild beasts devour the deathless Koshchei?'

'Where, then, is your death?' she asked.

'My death is over there; in that broom that stands by the threshold.'

As soon as Koshchei flew away, Vasilisa Kirbitievna ran to Prince Ivan, whereupon Bulat the Brave asked, 'Well, where is Koshchei's death?'

'It lies in a broom that stands by the threshold.'

'No, it does not. He has lied to you deliberately! You must question him again and this time exercise more cunning,' advised Bulat.

Vasilisa Kirbitievna hit upon a plan. She took the broom, coloured it with gold paint, ornamented it with bright ribbons, and laid it on the table. When Koshchei the Deathless flew back he saw the gilded broom on the table and, roaring with laughter, cried, 'What on earth made you do this?

Vasilisa answered, 'It seemed to me so disrespectful to have your death stand unceremoniously by the threshold. The table is a more dignified place for it.'

Koshchei could not hold his laughter and roared again when

he heard this. 'Ha, ha, ha, you ridiculous woman! Your hair may be long but your wit is short. Is it likely that my death lies here?'

'Where is it, then?'

'Why, my death is hidden in the goat.'

As soon as Koshchei flew away, Vasilisa Kirbitievna ran to Prince Ivan; whereupon Bulat the Brave again asked, 'Well, where is Koshchei's death?'

'It lies in the goat that gives me milk for my bath each morning and night.'

'No, it does not. He has once more deliberately lied to you. You must get the real truth out of him. Beware!'

So Vasilisa Kirbitievna did just as she had done with the broom. She adorned the goat with ribbons, hung bells around its neck, and gilded its horns. When Koshchei the Deathless flew back he saw the goat and, roaring with laughter, cried, 'Why have you done this to the goat?'

Vasilisa answered, 'It seemed so disrespectful to me to have your death in an ordinary old goat.' Koshchei could not hold his laughter and roared again when he heard this. 'Ha, ha, ha, you ridiculous woman! Your hair may be long but your wit is short. Is it likely that my death resides in a goat?'

'Where is it, then?'

'My death is to be found far, far away. In the middle of the sea there is an island; on that island is an oak tree; under the oak is buried a chest; in the chest is a hare; in the hare is a duck; in the duck is an egg; and in the egg is my death.' Having said these words, he flew away. Vasilisa Kirbitievna repeated every word to Prince Ivan and Bulat the Brave and this time they knew it to be the truth.

Taking with them a store of supplies, they set out to locate Koshchei's death. They travelled for a long time or a short time, until they had used up all their supplies and started to feel hungry. At that moment there passed by a dog with her litter of puppies. 'I will kill her,' said Bulat the Brave, 'for we shall die of hunger.'

'Do not kill me,' implored the dog, 'do not make orphans of my little ones. One day I may be of use to you.'

'Very well,' said Bulat, 'God be with you.' They continued walking toward the sea when they happened upon an eagle with her baby birds perched on the branch of an oak tree. Bulat the Brave said, 'I will kill the eagle, for we shall starve to death.'

'Do not kill me,' implored the eagle; 'do not make orphans of my little eaglets. One day I may be of use to you.'

'So be it,' said Bulat, 'live in health.' They finally reached the shore of a great sea and saw a lobster crawling along the beach. Bulat the Brave said, 'I will kill it, for we have found nothing to eat.'

'Do not kill me,' implored the lobster. 'There is not much of me, good fellow, so even if you do eat me you will be just as hungry. Please spare me, for one day I may be of use to you.'

'Well, crawl on, and God be with you,' said Bulat. Then looking out to sea he saw a fisherman fishing in his boat. 'Come here to shore,' he shouted.

The fisherman brought his boat to land. 'I am at your service, O travellers,' he said. So Prince Ivan and Bulat the Brave took their seats in the boat and rowed out to the island. They went to the oak, and Bulat wrenched the tree from its roots with his powerful arms. There he found the chest, just as Koshchei had described. As soon as they opened it a hare leapt out and ran off at a great speed.

'Alas,' groaned Prince Ivan, 'if only we had the dog here, it would fetch that hare for us.' No sooner had he said this than the grateful dog appeared as if from nowhere, chased after the runaway hare, captured it and presented it to him. Bulat the Brave seized the hare, tore it open and from its stomach flew a duck which soared high into the sky.

'Alas,' groaned Prince Ivan, 'if only we had the eagle here, it would fetch that duck for us.' No sooner had he said this than the grateful eagle swooped from the sky, captured the escaped duck and presented it to him. Bulat the Brave seized the duck, tore it open and from its stomach an egg rolled out and fell into the sea.

'Alas,' groaned the prince, 'if only we had the lobster here, it would drag that egg up for us.' No sooner had he said this than the grateful lobster crawled towards him carrying the egg. They took the egg and travelled back the way they had come. When they found Koshchei the Deathless, they smashed it on his forehead. In that instant he collapsed and died.

Prince Ivan then took the beautiful Vasilisa Kirbitievna and they headed off with Bulat the Brave toward their homeland. They rode on and on until night fell. Then they pitched a tent in a meadow and Vasilisa Kirbitievna lay down to sleep. Bulat the Brave said to Prince Ivan: 'You must sleep also, your Highness. Have no fear, I will keep watch.'

At midnight, twelve doves flew up with wings outstretched, one against the other's, and turned into twelve lovely damsels. 'Now then, Bulat the Brave and Prince Ivan,' they said, 'you have killed our brother, Koshchei the Deathless, and stolen his bride, Vasilisa Kirbitievna. Such behaviour will profit you little. For once Prince Ivan has settled back at home, he will command that his favourite dog be brought out; but it will break loose from the dog keeper and tear the prince into little pieces. Whoever hears this and reveals it to the prince will turn into stone up to the knees.'

In the morning Bulat the Brave woke the prince and Vasilisa Kirbitievna and in due course they made ready and resumed their journey. That second night they again pitched their tent in an open field. And once more Bulat the Brave said, 'Sleep, Prince Ivan, and have no fear, I will keep watch.'

As before, right at midnight, twelve doves flew up with wings outstretched, one against the other's, and turned into twelve lovely damsels. 'Well now, Bulat the Brave and Prince Ivan,' they said, 'you have killed our brother, Koshchei the Deathless, and stolen his bride, Vasilisa Kirbitievna. Such behaviour will profit you little. For once Prince Ivan has settled back at home, he will want to see his favourite horse, the one he has ridden since childhood. But it will break loose from the groom and kill the prince. Whoever hears this and reveals it to the prince will turn into stone up to the waist.'

The following morning they set off again. When it became dark they stopped to pitch their tent and spend their third night in the countryside. Bulat the Brave said, 'Prince Ivan, you must lie down to sleep and I will keep watch.'

Once again, in the blackness of midnight, twelve doves flew up with wings outstretched, one against the other's, and turned into twelve lovely damsels. 'So, Bulat the Brave and Prince Ivan,' they said, 'you have killed our brother, Koshchei the Deathless, and stolen his bride, Vasilisa Kirbitievna. Such behaviour will profit you little. For when Prince Ivan has settled back at home, he will wish to admire his favourite cow, whose milk he has drunk from childhood. But she will break loose from the cowherd and dig her horns into the prince. Whoever hears this and reveals it to the prince will turn into stone entirely.' Having spoken these words they changed back into doves and flew off.

Next morning the three travellers took the road for home. Upon their arrival the prince married Vasilisa Kirbitievna, and after a day or two said to her, 'Would you like to see my favourite dog? When I was a youngster we played together all the time.'

When he heard this, Bulat the Brave got hold of his sabre, sharpened it well, and approached the entrance to the palace. The dog was led out but, just as the maidens had said, it released itself from the dog keeper's grasp and ran straight to the front door. Bulat swung his sabre and in one stroke he cut the dog in two. Prince Ivan was very angry with Bulat the Brave, but said nothing on account of his past services.

On the next day the prince commanded that his favourite steed be led out. But the horse broke his halter, ran off from the groom and charged straight for the prince, rearing and thrashing with its hooves. Bulat the Brave swung his razor-edged sabre and in one stroke he cut off the horse's head. At that Prince Ivan's anger welled up in his breast.

'Seize the sword-bearer,' he commanded, 'and hang him!'

But Vasilisa Kirbitievna entreated and obtained his pardon. 'Remember,' she said, 'if it had not been for his assistance, you would never have won me.'

On the third day Prince Ivan instructed that his favourite cow be brought to him. She, too, fled from her keeper and ran violently toward the prince. At a stroke Bulat the Brave cut off her head. Prince Ivan was so furious that he would listen to no one. Immediately he ordered that the hangman be summoned for Bulat the Brave's execution.

'Ah, Prince Ivan,' said poor Bulat, 'now that you have commanded your executioner to put me to death, so may your will be done. But I would rather die by my own hand and not by that of another. By your leave might I say just three things?'

Bulat the Brave described the events of that first night when the twelve doves flew up to him and warned him about the things that would come to pass. At once he turned into stone up to the knees. Then he spoke of the second night, and became stone as high as his waist. Now Prince Ivan implored him with tears not to reveal the third. But Bulat the Brave answered, 'What difference does it make? I am already half stone; life is no longer worth living.' And relating the happenings of the third night he turned completely into a statue of stone. Prince Ivan solemnly placed him in a special chamber where he and his wife visited him each day and they both wept bitterly.

Many years went by and then one day, while Prince Ivan was lamenting over the petrified Bulat, he heard a deep voice ring out from the statue: 'Why are you crying?' said the voice. 'Isn't my situation desperate enough without your weeping?'

'How can I not weep? Is it not because of me that you were turned into stone?'

'If you wish, there is one way you can save me.'

'I will do anything. Please tell me.'

'You have two young children, a son and a daughter. Take them, slay them, draw their blood, gather it, and smear my stone with it.'

Prince Ivan told this to Vasilisa Kirbitievna and, after much grieving and weeping, they consented to sacrifice their children. They took them, slew them, drew their blood, gathered it and smeared the stone statue with it. All at once life returned to Bulat the Brave. He asked the prince and his wife: 'Are you not broken-hearted over your children?'

'We are, Bulat, our eyes are worn out with weeping.'

'Well, then, let us go to their chambers.' On entering, they saw that the children were alive and well. Both father and mother were overjoyed, and in their excitement they held a banquet for everyone. I was at that celebration, too, and drank mead and wine. It ran down my moustache but not into my mouth; yet my soul was quenched and sated.

Vasilisa the Beautiful and Baba Yaga

In a certain kingdom there lived a merchant and his wife. Although they had been married for twelve years, they had only one daughter, the beautiful Vasilisa. When the girl was eight years old her mother contracted a serious illness, and on her deathbed she called her daughter to her side. Taking a doll from under her bed clothes she gave it to the girl and said, 'Listen, dear Vasilisa, remember these my last words. I am leaving this world and together with my blessings I bequeath to you this doll. Keep it with you always but show it to no one. If at any time you get into trouble, give the doll some nourishment and ask its advice.' Then the merchant's wife kissed her daughter, gave a deep sigh and died.

After his wife's death, the merchant grieved as is proper, and then began to consider the prospect of remarriage. He was a handsome man and would have no difficulty in finding a wife. Indeed, he was somewhat attracted to a certain middle-aged widow who had two daughters of her own, about the same age as Vasilisa. The widow had a reputation for being a good housekeeper and mother to her daughters. But after the merchant married her he soon realized that he had been deceived, for she was unkind to Vasilisa. Vasilisa was the most beautiful girl in the village, and her stepmother and stepsisters were envious of her. They persecuted her and tormented her by forcing her to do laborious tasks, hoping that she would suffer from the toil, grow thin and turn brown from over-exposure to the wind and sun. But Vasilisa endured all of this without complaint, and every day she became lovelier. By contrast, the stepmother and her daughters, who sat idly with folded hands like noble ladies, grew pale and ugly from spite.

What was Vasilisa's secret? Without the help of her doll she could not have overcome the daily chores. Every day, Vasilisa did not eat all of her food, but would keep dainty morsels for her doll. And in the evening, when everyone had fallen asleep, she would lock herself in her small bedroom, give the doll the treat she had saved, and say, 'Now, dear dolly, eat and listen to my tale of woe. Although I live in my father's house, there is no happiness in my life. A wicked stepmother makes my world a misery. Tell me how and what I should do.' Once the doll had swallowed the food, it would give advice to the sorrowful child, comfort her in her sorrow, and in the morning would complete all of Vasilisa's tasks. Thus Vasilisa could rest in the shade or pick her favourite flowers while the garden was weeded, the cabbage patch watered, the water carried in and the stove heated. The doll even showed the young girl a herb that would protect her fair skin from the elements. Thanks to her doll, Vasilisa spent her days without effort.

As the years passed Vasilisa grew up and was courted by all the young men in the village. Not one, however, ever cast a glance at either of her stepsisters. To make matters difficult, the stepmother became ever more spiteful and would answer the suitors with the following words: 'I will not allow my youngest daughter to marry before the elder ones.' After dismissing each suitor, she vented her anger on Vasilisa with harsh words and cruel blows.

It happened that one day the merchant was required to leave home for a long time in order to do business in a distant country. In the meantime, his wife moved to another house, close to a dense forest. In the glade of that forest there stood a hut, and in the hut lived Baba Yaga, the witch. She refused admittance to one and all and if anyone wandered near her home, she ate them as if they were chickens.

As soon as the jealous stepmother was settled in the new house, she repeatedly found one pretext after another to send the hated Vasilisa into the wood. But each time she did so the girl returned home safe and sound, because her doll had guided her and made sure that she kept a good distance from Baba Yaga's hut.

With the coming of autumn the stepmother allocated an evening task to each of her three daughters. One was required to make lace, another to knit stockings, and Vasilisa had to spin. One evening, the stepmother extinguished the lights all over the house, except for one candle in the room where the girls sat at work. She then went to bed while the others continued working. Eventually, the candle began to smoke and needed attention, so one of the stepsisters took up a pair of scissors to trim it. As if by accident she snuffed out the light.

'What are we to do now?' said the girls. 'There is no light anywhere in the house and our tasks are still unfinished. Someone must run to Baba Yaga for a light.'

'I do not need to go,' said the daughter who was making lace, 'because I can see my pins and they reflect enough light.'

'Neither shall I go,' said the daughter who was knitting stockings, 'my bright knitting needles give me all the light I need.'

'Then you must fetch the light,' both of them cried to their stepsister. 'Go to Baba Yaga's.' And they pushed Vasilisa from the room.

The poor girl went to her small bedroom, placed down the supper she had prepared for her doll, and said, 'Now, dolly, eat up and hear my trouble. My stepsisters are sending me to Baba Yaga's for a light, and she will eat me up.' The doll feasted on the meal and its eyes glowed like two lanterns.

'Have no fear, Vasilisa,' answered the doll. 'Perform your errand, but keep me with you the whole time. While I am in your pocket, Baba Yaga will not harm you.' Vasilisa got herself ready, placed the doll in her apron pocket, made the sign of the cross, and entered the dense forest, trembling all the while.

It seemed as though no time had passed before suddenly a horseman galloped past her. His face was white, his clothes were white, his horse was white, and so were its saddle and bridle. The dawn light entered the woods. The girl continued walking further and another horseman galloped past her: he was completely red, dressed in red and his horse was red. The sun began to rise above the trees.

Vasilisa walked all day, all night and again all day, and it was only on the third evening that she found the glade where Baba Yaga's hut stood. The fence around the hut was made of human bones, and on the posts were fixed human skulls with staring eyes. Instead of door posts at the gates, there were human legs; instead of bolts there were human hands and instead of a lock there was a mouth with sharp teeth. Vasilisa froze in horror and stood rooted to the spot.

Suddenly another horseman rode past. He was entirely black, dressed in black, and rode a black horse. He galloped through Baba Yaga's gates and vanished, as if Moist Mother Earth had consumed him. Night fell. But the darkness did not last long. The eyes in all the skulls on the fence began to glow and at once it became as light as day throughout the glade. Vasilisa quaked from fear, but not knowing where to run, she remained transfixed.

Very shortly a deafening sound resounded through the forest. The trees crackled, the dry leaves rustled, and from the woods Baba Yaga appeared riding in a mortar which she drove with a pestle, while she swept away traces of her progress with a broom. She rode up to the gates and stopped. Sniffing the air about her, she cried, 'Fie, fie! I smell the smell of a Russian! Who is here?'

Vasilisa advanced towards the old woman in fear and trembling and bowing low to her, said, 'It is I, grandmother. My stepsisters have sent me to you for a light.'

'Very well,' said Baba Yaga, 'I know them. But before I give you a light, you must first of all live with me and do some work. If you refuse, I will eat you up.' Then she turned to the gates and cried out, 'Ho, my strong bolts, unlock! Open up, my wide gates!' The gates opened and Baba Yaga went in whistling. Vasilisa followed her and then everything closed up again.

The witch entered the room, stretched herself out in her chair and said to Vasilisa, 'Bring me what is in the stove, for I am hungry.' Vasilisa lit a torch from the skulls on the fence and began to serve the food from the stove. The meal would have been enough to satisfy ten men. In addition, Vasilisa went to the cellar and brought up kvas, mead, beer and wine. The old woman ate and drank almost everything, leaving nothing for Vasilisa other than some morsels, a little cabbage soup and crusts of bread, and tiny pieces of suckling pig.

Then Baba Yaga prepared to go to bed and said, 'Tomorrow after I leave, see to it that you clean the yard, sweep out the hut, cook the dinner and wash the linen. Then go to the corn bin, take a bushel of wheat and separate the chaff. See that all is done, otherwise I shall eat you up.'

Having given these commands, Baba Yaga began to snore. Whereupon Vasilisa placed the leftovers of the old witch's supper before her doll and, weeping bitterly, said, 'Now, dolly, eat up this food and hear my plight. Baba Yaga has set me a difficult task and threatens to eat me up if I fail in any way. Help me!'

The doll answered, 'Have no fear, beautiful Vasilisa! Eat your supper, say your prayers and lie down to sleep; the morning is wiser than the evening.'

Vasilisa awoke very early the next morning, but Baba Yaga had already risen and was looking out of the window. There outside on the fence, the light from the eyes of the skulls was dimming; then the white horseman dashed by, and day broke. Baba Yaga went out in the yard, whistled, and suddenly before her appeared the mortar with a pestle and a hearth broom. The red horseman flashed by, and the sun rose. Then Baba Yaga took her place in the mortar and drove it forward with the pestle, sweeping away traces of her progress with the broom.

The beautiful Vasilisa remained alone within. As she looked around Baba Yaga's hut, she was astonished at her immense wealth and the abundance of everything. Which task was she to begin with? In despair, Vasilisa closed her eyes. Was it only for a moment? When she looked again, behold, all the work had been done and the doll was finishing the job of separating the last shreds of chaff from the wheat.

'Oh my saviour,' said Vasilisa to the doll, 'you have delivered me from death.'

'There is only one thing left, and that is for you to do,' answered the doll, crawling back into Vasilisa's pocket. 'Cook the dinner; cook it with God's help, and then take a rest.'

When evening came Vasilisa laid the table and awaited the old woman's return. Twilight began to fall, the black horseman flashed by the gates, and it grew completely dark. Only the skulls' eyes were shining. The trees crackled and the leaves rustled: Baba Yaga was coming. Vasilisa met her.

'Is everything done?' asked Baba Yaga.

'Please see for yourself, grandmother,' said Vasilisa. The witch examined everything and, annoyed that she had nothing to complain about, said, 'Very well then.' Then she cried, 'My faithful servants and bosom friends, grind my wheat!' Three pairs of hands appeared, seized the wheat and carried it out of sight.

Baba Yaga ate her fill, prepared for sleep and again issued instructions to Vasilisa: 'Do tomorrow exactly the same tasks that you performed today, but in addition, take the poppy seeds from the bin and remove the earth from them, grain by grain. For some spiteful person has thrown earth into the seed bin.' And the old witch turned to the wall and began to snore.

Vasilisa began to feed her doll who, once satisfied, spoke as she had spoken the day before: 'Pray to God and go to sleep; the morning is wiser than the evening. Everything will be done, dear Vasilisa.'

The following morning Baba Yaga again departed from the yard in her mortar and immediately Vasilisa and the doll set to work at their tasks. When the old woman returned that evening, she looked carefully at everything and cried out, 'My faithful servants and bosom friends, press the oil from the poppy seeds!' Three pairs of hands appeared, seized the poppy seeds and carried them out of sight. Baba Yaga sat down to eat, and while she ate Vasilisa stood silent.

'Why do you stand there so silently?' asked Baba Yaga. 'You act as if you were dumb.'

'I did not have the courage to speak,' replied Vasilisa, 'but with your permission I would like to ask you a question.'

'Do so; but remember not every question has a good answer. If you learn too much, you will soon grow old.'

'I only want to ask you, grandmother, about what I have seen. As I was on my way to you a white horseman, dressed in white and on a white horse, overtook me. Who is he?'

'He is my bright day,' answered Baba Yaga.

'Then another horseman overtook me. He was totally red, dressed in red, and had a red steed. Who is he?'

'He is my red sun,' came the answer.

'And who is the black horseman who flashed past me at your gate, grandmother?'

'He is my dark night. And all three are my faithful servants.'

Vasilisa remembered the three pairs of hands, but kept silent.

'Have you no more questions to ask?' said Baba Yaga.

'Yes, indeed,' said Vasilisa, 'but you said yourself, grandmother, that the more I learn the older I shall become.'

'It is well,' said the witch, 'that you have asked only about things seen outside my hut, and not about anything within. I do not like to expose my dirty washing, and I take pleasure in eating people who are over-curious. Now I shall ask you something. How do you manage to perform all the tasks I set for you?'

'I am aided by the blessing of my dear mother,' answered Vasilisa.

'Blessing? Blessing! So that is what it is! Begone then, blessed daughter,' shrieked Baba Yaga, 'I shall have no blessed people in my hut.' The old woman dragged Vasilisa out of the room and pushed her outside the gate. Taking a skull with burning eyes from the fence and sticking it on a pole, she gave it to the girl, saying, 'Here is the light for your stepsisters. Take it; this is what they sent you for.'

Vasilisa ran homeward, with the skull's light to direct her steps. All night it shone, and only went out during the day. At last, by nightfall of the second day, she reached her home. As she approached the gates, she thought about abandoning the skull. 'Surely,' she thought, 'light will no longer be needed in the house.'

But suddenly a hollow voice came from the skull and said, 'Do not throw me away, but take me to your stepmother.' Vasilisa looked at the house and saw that no light shone in any of the windows, so she decided to enter with the skull.

To begin with her stepmother and stepsisters greeted her courteously. 'Since you left, Vasilisa, we have been without light and fire. We were unable to strike a flame in any way and if any of our neighbours brought a light in, it went out the moment it was carried into the house. Perhaps your light will last,' said the stepmother. When they brought the skull into the room it fixed its brightly shining eyes on the stepmother and her daughters, and kept staring at them. All their efforts to hide themselves were in vain. Wherever they went they were ceaselessly pursued by the eyes. By sunrise they had all been burned to ashes; only Vasilisa remained unharmed by the fire.

In the morning Vasilisa buried the skull in the moist earth, locked up the house, and went into town. She went to the house of a certain childless old woman. 'Grandmother, give me shelter while I wait for my father's return,' she begged. The old woman took her in, and they lived quietly together.

One day she said to the woman, 'It wearies me to sit idly, grandmother. If you would buy me some good flax, I shall busy myself with spinning.' The old woman bought some of the best flax and Vasilisa sat down to spin. She spun at lightning speed, and the thread when spun was as even and fine as a small hair. The yarn began to pile high and it was time to start weaving it, but there was no comb fine enough for Vasilisa's thread and nobody would undertake to make one.

So Vasilisa resorted to her doll for assistance. 'Bring me an old comb that has belonged to a weaver, and an old shuttle, and a horse's mane,' advised the doll, 'and I will do everything for you.' Vasilisa obtained all that was required and then lay down to rest. During the night the doll made a wonderful loom for her. By the end of winter, the linen had been woven. Its texture was so fine that it could be drawn through a needle like a thread. In the spring the linen was bleached, and Vasilisa said to the old woman, 'Grandmother, sell this linen and keep the money for yourself.' The old woman looked at the work and sighed, 'No, my child! For nobody but the tsar can wear such linen. I shall take it to the palace.'

The old woman went to the royal buildings and paced up and down beneath the windows. When the tsar saw her he asked, 'What is it that you want, old woman?'

'Your Majesty,' she answered, 'I have brought some wonderful merchandise and will show it to nobody other than you.' The tsar commanded that she be brought in before him, and he marvelled when he saw the linen.

'How much do you want for it?' enquired the tsar.

'It is beyond price, father Tsar. I have brought it as a gift to you.' The tsar thanked her and rewarded her with many presents.

The tsar ordered that shirts be cut from the linen. This was done, but a seamstress could nowhere be found who was willing to complete the sewing. For many weeks the palace officials tried to find one, but finally the tsar summoned the old woman and said to her, 'Since you were able to spin and weave such linen, you must know how to sew shirts from it.'

'But your Majesty, it was not I who spun and wove this linen; it is the work of a fair damsel to whom I have given shelter.'

'Well, then, let her sew them,' commanded the tsar.

The old woman returned home and related everything to Vasilisa. The girl said in reply, 'I knew all along that my work was not yet finished.' She shut herself in her room and set to work; she sewed without resting her hands and soon a dozen shirts were ready. The old woman took them to the tsar while Vasilisa washed herself, combed her hair, dressed in her finest clothes and then took a seat at the window, there to await events. Eventually she spotted a servant of the tsar entering the old woman's courtyard. The messenger came into the room and said, 'The tsar wishes to see the skilled needlewoman who made his shirts. He desires to reward her out of his royal hands.' Vasilisa presented herself before the tsar and when the tsar saw her he was totally overcome by her beauty. 'You must never leave my side; you shall be my wife,' he cried. He took Vasilisa by her white hands, seated her by his side and the wedding was celebrated at once.

In due course, Vasilisa's father returned to rejoice at his daughter's good fortune, and came to live with her. Vasilisa also brought the old woman into her palace and took care of her. Most important of all, Vasilisa never parted with her little doll, which she carried in her pocket till the end of her life.

Prince Ivan, the Firebird and the Grey Wolf

In a certain kingdom in a certain land there lived a tsar called Vyslav Andronovich who had three sons named Prince Dimitri, Prince Vasili and Prince Ivan. The tsar had a garden so rich and abundant, there was none like it in any realm. Among the many valuable and rare trees in this garden – both with and without fruit – was one that was especially prized by the tsar. It was an apple tree that bore beautiful golden apples.

It happened that a firebird took to visiting Tsar Vyslav's garden every evening. Her wings were of gold and her eyes like sparkling crystals of the orient, and she would fly into the tree, perch on a bough and pick the beautiful golden fruit. Then she would fly away, only to return the following evening to feast on the precious apples. The tsar was greatly distressed at the diminishing number of apples on the tree, so he summoned his three sons and said to them, 'My beloved children, can any one of you catch the firebird that is attacking my favourite apple tree? Whoever captures the bird alive will receive one half of my kingdom here and now, while I yet live; and when I die he will inherit the rest.'

Then his sons, the three princes, shouted in response with one voice, 'Gracious sovereign and father, we will endeavour with pleasure to capture the firebird alive.'

The first night Prince Dimitri kept watch in the garden and stood by the apple tree from which the firebird had been plucking the golden apples. He waited and waited and eventually fell asleep and so did not notice the firebird enter the garden, fly into the tree and pick the precious fruit. The next morning Tsar Vyslav called Dimitri and asked him, 'Well, my dear son, did you or did you not see the firebird?'

'No, gracious sovereign and father,' he replied, 'for the firebird did not come last night.'

The next night Prince Vasili kept watch in the garden and stood by the same apple tree. But barely had two hours elapsed before he fell fast asleep and so he did not notice the firebird enter the garden, fly into the tree and pick the precious fruit. The following morning Tsar Vyslav called Vasili and asked him, 'Well, my dear son, did you or did you not see the firebird?'

'No, gracious sovereign and father,' he replied, 'for the firebird did not come last night.'

The third night Prince Ivan kept watch in the garden and stood by the same apple tree. He remained alert for one hour, then two and then three – then suddenly the entire garden was flooded with light as if by many flames. Down flew the marvellous firebird; she alighted on one of the boughs of the apple tree and began to pick the priceless fruit. With great cunning and caution, Prince Ivan crept up to her, stretched out his arm and made a sudden grasp. But the bird was too quick for him; she tore herself free and flew off in fright. All that was left in Prince Ivan's clenched fist was one brightly coloured tail feather.

Early the next morning the prince rushed into his father's room. 'Well, my dear son, did you or did you not see the firebird?'

'Yes, gracious sovereign and father,' replied Ivan, 'the firebird did come last night and here is a feather from her tail. She will never trespass in your garden again.'

Tsar Vyslav was greatly delighted that his youngest son had been able to retrieve even one small feather from the firebird's tail. And what a feather it was! When placed in a darkened room it glowed marvellously and shone with the light of a thousand candles. The tsar treasured this relic, for a thing so marvellous, he thought, should be preserved for all time.

'If but one small feather can possess such extraordinary beauty,' mused Tsar Vyslav, 'what must the entire bird be like?' An idea suddenly possessed him. He again summoned the three princes and said to them, 'My dear children, I offer you my blessing to set out on an urgent mission. Go forth and seek out the fabulous firebird. Bring her to me alive, and what I had promised at first will surely go to the one who succeeds.'

Now Prince Dimitri and Prince Vasili bore malice against their younger brother, Prince Ivan, because he had been able to seize a feather from the firebird's tail. They were determined to get the better of him this time so, taking their father's blessing, they rode swiftly away together to capture the firebird.

'Give me your blessing, too, father,' said Ivan, 'that I may set out on the quest.'

But Tsar Vyslav was reluctant to permit the young prince to undertake a task that could lead to danger. 'My beloved son,' he said, 'you are still too young and inexperienced to embark upon such a long and difficult journey. Why should you leave my house?

After all, your brothers have already left. What if you, too, were to depart and none of you should return for a very long time? I am old now and walk in the shadow of God. If, during your absence, the Lord takes my life, who would there be to take my place and rule the kingdom? What if a rebellion were to break out, or disturbances among our subjects? There would be nobody with authority to restore order. And if an enemy were to approach our dominions, there would be nobody to command our forces.'

But no matter how hard Tsar Vyslav tried to restrain his son, he could not withhold the blessing that was sought, for Prince Ivan was stubbornly insistent. The young man immediately selected a fine horse and set out on his journey even though he knew not where he was going.

Randomly taking a dusty path, he proceeded uphill and downhill, near and far, along byways and throughways. (The tale is quickly told, but the deed is not quickly done.) Eventually he reached wide, open country and rode onto a grassy meadow. In front of him he spotted a tall stone pillar on which were written these words: 'Whoever continues straight on past this pillar will become cold and hungry; whoever turns to the right will keep strong and healthy, but his horse will be killed; whoever turns to the left will himself be killed, but his horse will be safe and sound.' Having read this inscription, Prince Ivan decided to go to the right, bearing in mind that although his horse might be killed, he himself would remain alive and would in time get another horse.

He travelled for one entire day, then for a second and finally for a third. All at once an enormous grey wolf leaped towards him and said, 'Aha, so it is you, my good young man, Prince Ivan! Why have you come this way? Did you not see the message on the pillar that warned of your horse's death?' The wolf uttered these words, tore the prince's horse in two and departed.

Prince Ivan lamented bitterly the loss of his horse, but continued his journey on foot. He walked the entire day and became unspeakably exhausted. Just as he was about to sit down and rest for a moment, the grey wolf quite suddenly appeared and said, 'I am extremely sorry, Prince Ivan, that you are so tired from walking and I also regret having destroyed your fine horse. So please mount me, the grey wolf, and tell me where I may take you and for what purpose.'

The prince climbed on the wolf's back and told him the whole story about the firebird and the tsar's commands. The grey wolf sped off with him more swiftly than any horse could have carried him and by nightfall they arrived at a low stone wall.

'Now, Prince Ivan, climb down from me, the grey wolf, and quickly scale that stone wall. Behind it you will discover a beautiful garden, and in that garden sits the firebird that you seek. She is sitting in a gilded cage. Take the firebird, but I warn you, do not touch the golden cage. If you attempt to remove it, you will be unable to escape but will be caught straight away.'

Prince Ivan climbed over the stone wall into the garden, spotted the firebird in her gilded cage, and was totally captivated by her appearance and by the beauty of the cage. He removed the bird from the cage and began retracing his steps when he stopped in his tracks and thought, 'Why have I taken the firebird without her cage? Where shall I put her?' So he returned, and no sooner did he lay his hand on the cage than there was a hammering sound accompanied by a thunderous noise that echoed throughout the garden, for warning wires had been attached to the bird's golden cage. At once the watchmen woke up, ran into the garden, apprehended Prince Ivan with the firebird and took him to their king, whose name was Dolmat.

Dolmat was greatly incensed at the prince and shouted at him in a fierce and furious voice: 'What is this! Young man, are you not ashamed to steal? What is your name, who is your father and from which land have you come?'

'I am Prince Ivan, the son of Tsar Vyslav Andronovich, and have come from his kingdom. Your firebird made a habit of flying to our royal garden each night to pluck the golden apples from my father's favourite tree. She has ruined practically the entire tree. This is why my father sent me to locate the thieving firebird and take her to him.'

'Oh, young man, Prince Ivan! Do you really consider this to be the correct way for a person of your position to go about things? You ought to have come straight to me and made your request; I would have presented the firebird to you with honour. But now, how will it seem to you when I inform all the neighbouring kingdoms of your dishonourable actions! However, listen carefully, Prince Ivan. If you render me a special service, I will pardon you your offence and give you the firebird with all honour. Go beyond the thrice-nine lands to the thrice-tenth kingdom and get for me from Tsar Aphron his golden-maned steed. If you refuse me this, I will let it be known in all parts how despicably you have behaved in my kingdom and that you are a miserable thief.' Prince Ivan was greatly distressed. He promised to procure for King Dolmat the horse with the golden mane, and took his leave of him.

He went back to the grey wolf and reported to him all that Tsar Dolmat had said. 'Ah, Prince Ivan, young man,' said the grey wolf, 'why did you disobey my instructions? Why did you attempt to take the gilded cage?'

'It is true; I am guilty of a serious offence and I acknowledge my fault,' said the prince humbly.

'Very well; so be it,' said the grey wolf. 'Now mount on me, the grey wolf, and I shall take you wherever you wish to go.' The Prince did so and the grey wolf sped off like lightning, a short distance or a long one, toward the eastern sky. At dusk they entered the realm of Tsar Aphron and eventually came to the white-walled imperial stables. The grey wolf said, 'You must go alone into these white-walled stables, Prince Ivan, but have no fear, the guards are fast asleep. Take the golden-maned steed which you will find in the furthest stall. But heed this warning, do not lay a finger on the golden bridle that hangs on the wall. Otherwise great misfortune will befall you.'

Prince Ivan entered the white-walled stables, took the horse and began retracing his steps when he stopped in his tracks and thought, 'What an exquisite bridle. Without it, how can I lead this noble beast?' So he removed it from the wall. Instantly a noise like thunder resounded through the stables because alarm wires had been attached to that bridle. The stable guards woke up at once, rushed in, seized Prince Ivan and conducted him to Tsar Aphron. The tsar began to interrogate him, 'Ah, my young fellow, which kingdom do you come from, whose son are you and what is your name?'

'I am Prince Ivan, the son of Tsar Vyslav Andronovich, and have come from his kingdom.'

'Oh, young man, Prince Ivan! Do you really consider this to be the correct way for a person of your position to act? You ought to have come straight to me and made your request; I would have presented the horse with the golden mane to you with honour. But now, how will it seem to you when I inform all the neighbouring kingdoms of your dishonourable actions? However, listen carefully Prince Ivan. If you render me a special service, if you will go beyond the thrice-nine lands to the thrice-tenth kingdom and get for me Princess Elena the Fair, with whom I long ago fell totally in love, heart and soul, but whom I cannot secure for my wife, I will pardon you your offence and give you the horse with the golden mane with all honour. But if you refuse me this, I will let it be known in all parts how despicably you have behaved in my kingdom and that you are a miserable thief.' Prince Ivan promised Tsar Aphron to secure Princess Elena the Fair and then left the palace weeping bitterly.

He went back to the grey wolf and reported to him all that Tsar Aphron had said. 'Ah, Prince Ivan, young man,' said the grey wolf, 'why did you disobey my instructions? Why did you attempt to take the golden bridle?'

'It is true; I am again guilty of a serious offence and I acknowledge my fault,' said the prince humbly.

'Very well; so be it,' said the grey wolf. 'Now mount on me, the grey wolf, and I shall take you wherever you wish to go.' The prince mounted and the grey wolf sped off like lightning, so that in an amazingly short time they reached the kingdom of Elena the Fair.

When they came to the golden fence that surrounded the wonderful garden, the wolf said to Ivan, 'Now, my Prince Ivan, dismount from me, the grey wolf, and go back along the very same road along which we came. Wait for me in the open countryside under a green oak tree.'

Prince Ivan went where he was commanded while the grey wolf crouched down by the golden fence and waited until Elena the Fair should come to take her evening stroll in the garden. Toward evening, as the sun was sinking low in the western sky and the night air lost its warmth, Princess Elena the Fair set out on her walk through the garden. She was attended by maidens from the court and her ladies-in-waiting. As the princess approached the spot by the fence where the grey wolf was lying in wait, he suddenly jumped out, seized her, sprang back again and bore her away at full speed.

When he met up with Prince Ivan, who was patiently waiting for him in the open countryside under the green oak tree, he shouted an order: 'My prince, leap up on my back immediately and seat yourself on me, the grey wolf.' Prince Ivan mounted the wolf and the grey wolf sped off, bearing them both along to the territory of Tsar Aphron.

The court maidens and the ladies-in-waiting that had accompanied Princess Elena the Fair on her walk in the garden reported the events immediately to the palace. At a moment's notice men-at-arms were commanded to pursue and overtake the grey wolf; but no matter how fast they ran, they could not outrun him and were forced to return empty-handed.

While sitting beside Elena the Fair on the grey wolf's back, Prince Ivan fell totally in love with her, and she also began to love him. Thus by the time the grey wolf entered Tsar Aphron's domain, and Prince Ivan was obliged to conduct the princess to the palace and present her to the tsar, he had become very sullen and began to lament and to weep bitter tears. 'Why are you weeping so, Prince Ivan?' asked the grey wolf.

'Oh, grey wolf, my dear friend, how can a young fellow such as I not weep and grieve? I have fallen in love with Elena the Fair with all my heart and soul, and now I must render her up to Tsar Aphron in return for the horse with the golden mane. For if I fail to do this, the tsar will dishonour me far and wide.'

'I have been of much service to you, Prince Ivan,' said the grey wolf, 'but I shall do one more favour for you. Listen to my plan, O prince. I will transform myself into the fair Elena and you must take me to the Tsar Aphron, who will imagine that I am a real princess. Then take from him the horse with the golden mane. Later, when you have mounted the noble horse and ridden off into the distance, I shall seek permission from Tsar Aphron to take a walk in the open field with my companions and ladies-in-waiting. After that, all you need to do is call me to remembrance and I shall again be at your side.'

Having uttered these words, the grey wolf struck himself against Moist Mother Earth and became the image and likeness of Princess Elena the Fair so that it was impossible to distinguish in any way that the wolf was not the princess. Prince Ivan instructed Elena the Fair to wait for him outside the town, and led the grey wolf to the palace of Tsar Aphron. When the prince presented the false Elena the Fair to the tsar, he immediately rejoiced with all his heart that he had taken possession of the treasure which he had so long desired. Accepting the beautiful impostor, the tsar gave Prince Ivan the horse with the golden mane. The prince immediately mounted the steed and rode out of the town to his fair Elena whom he seated behind him; thereupon he set his course to the kingdom of Tsar Dolmat.

As for the grey wolf, he remained with Tsar Aphron for one day, a second day, and then a third, in the place of Elena the Fair. But on the fourth day he went to Tsar Aphron and requested his permission to take a walk outside in the open field, 'to drive away the cruel grief and sorrow' that had befallen him.

Tsar Aphron spoke these words to him: 'Ah, my most precious and fair Princess Elena. Your wish is my command; I would do anything for you. Of course you may go for a stroll in the open field.' And straight away he commanded the palace maids and ladies-in-waiting to accompany the fair princess on a walk in the open field.

Meanwhile, Prince Ivan was riding along the highways and by-ways with the true Princess Elena, talking to her the whole time and almost forgetting about the grey wolf. However, he suddenly remembered, exclaiming, 'Oh, where can my grey wolf be?'

In the twinkling of an eye, as if from nowhere, the grey wolf appeared before him and said, 'Prince Ivan, mount on me, the grey wolf, and allow the lovely Princess Elena to ride the horse with the golden mane.' Prince Ivan sat on the grey wolf and they rode toward the kingdom of Tsar Dolmat.

After travelling a long time or a short time, they approached the kingdom and stopped two miles from the main town. Prince Ivan began to beseech the grey wolf, saying, 'My dear friend, grey wolf, please listen to my words. You have been of much service to me and I am extremely grateful. Now do me one last favour. Would it not be possible for you to take on the appearance of a golden-maned horse in place of this one? For I greatly desire to have my own horse with a golden mane.' Immediately the grey wolf struck himself against Moist Mother Earth and became the image and likeness of a horse with a golden mane.

Leaving Princess Elena the Fair in a green meadow, Prince Ivan climbed onto the grey wolf and entered the wide palace courtyard of Tsar Dolmat. As soon as the tsar saw Prince Ivan approaching on the horse with the golden mane he rejoiced greatly. In a few moments he rushed down to meet the prince in the wide courtyard, embraced him fondly, led him by the right hand and brought him into the white-walled palace hall. To celebrate this joyous event, Tsar Dolmat held a great feast at which all the guests sat at oaken tables with checked tablecloths. Everyone ate, drank, laughed and made merry for precisely two days. And on the third day, Tsar Dolmat presented to the prince the firebird in its golden cage. Together with the firebird, Ivan journeyed outside the town, mounted the true golden-maned steed alongside Princess Elena the Fair and set out for his homeland, the kingdom of Tsar Vyslav Andronovich.

As for Tsar Dolmat, he decided the next day to break in his golden-maned horse out in the open field. He ordered his aides to saddle the steed, then he mounted it and rode off to the open field. But his actions irritated the horse, which threw Tsar Dolmat from his back. The horse then became the grey wolf again, raced away and caught up with Prince Ivan. 'Prince Ivan,' he said, 'mount on me, the grey wolf, and allow the lovely Princess Elena to ride the horse with the golden mane.' Prince Ivan sat on the grey wolf and they rode toward the kingdom of Tsar Vyslav. As soon as the grey wolf had brought Prince Ivan to the spot where he had torn his horse in two, he stopped and said: 'Now, Prince Ivan, I have served you long enough in faith and truth. Here is the place where I tore your horse in two, and I have returned you to the same spot safe and sound. Dismount from me, the grey wolf, for now you have the horse with the golden mane; sit on him and go wherever you must. I am no longer your servant.' With these words the grey wolf departed quickly; Prince Ivan bitterly bewailed the loss of his faithful wolf and continued his journey with the beautiful princess.

He travelled with Princess Elena for a long time or for a short time on the horse with the golden mane until, having come within fifteen miles of his home city, he stopped, climbed down from his horse and lay down to rest from the heat of the sun beneath an oak tree, with the fair princess at his side. He tethered the horse with the golden mane to the same tree and put down the cage with the firebird by his side. Lying on the soft grass and carrying on a pleasant conversation, they both fell soundly asleep.

Just at that time Prince Dimitri and Prince Vasili, the brothers of Prince Ivan, who had travelled through various kingdoms without finding the firebird, were returning home with empty hands. Quite unexpectedly, they came upon their sleeping brother, Prince Ivan, with the fair princess. At the same time they saw the horse with the golden mane and the firebird in its golden cage and became extremely envious and sorely tempted and thought of slaying their brother, Ivan. Prince Dimitri drew his sword from its scabbard, stabbed Prince Ivan and cut him into little pieces; then he roused Elena the Fair and began to interrogate her: 'Maiden most lovely,' he said, 'from which dominion have you come? Who is your father and what is your name?'

When Princess Elena the Fair saw Prince Ivan lying dead, she began to shed bitter tears, saying, 'I am Princess Elena the Fair; I was carried off by Prince Ivan whom you have put to a cruel death. Had you been more heroic knights, you would have gone with him into an open field and conquered him in fair combat. But you have slain him while he was sleeping. What praise and fame will you receive for that? A sleeping man is the same as a dead one.'

Thereupon Prince Dimitri pressed the sharp point of his sword against the heart of Princess Elena and said, 'Take heed, Elena the Fair, you are now at our mercy and we shall take you to our father, Tsar Vyslav Andronovich. You must inform him that it was we who captured you as well as the firebird and the horse with the golden mane. If you do not promise to say this, you shall surely die immediately at my hands.'

Frightened by the threat of death, the fair princess gave the promise and swore by everything sacred that she would speak as commanded. Then Prince Dimitri and Prince Vasili began to cast lots to see who should get Elena the Fair, and who should get the horse with the golden mane; and the lots so fell that Prince Vasili obtained the fair princess and Prince Dimitri the horse with the golden mane. Prince Vasili took Elena the Fair and seated her on his noble steed while Prince Dimitri mounted the horse with the golden mane and picked up the caged firebird in order to hand it to his father, Tsar Vyslav Andronovich, and they all set out on their way.

Prince Ivan lay dead on that spot for exactly thirty days and thirty nights. At the end of this time the grey wolf came by him and recognized him by his scent. The wolf wanted to aid the prince, to bring him back to life, but knew not how to do it. At that moment he looked up into the sky and caught sight of a certain raven with its two young who were flying above the body of Prince Ivan, preparing themselves to swoop earthwards and satisfy their hunger by eating the dead prince's flesh. The grey wolf concealed himself behind a bush and when the ravens descended and readied themselves to begin eating the body, he pounced forward, seized one of the young ravens and prepared to tear him in two. Then the mother raven alighted on Moist Mother Earth but kept a careful distance from the grey wolf and called out to him, 'Greetings, grey wolf; do not harm my young child; he has done nothing to you.'

'Listen quite carefully to me, raven,' growled the wolf, 'I shall not touch your child and will release it unharmed if you will render me a service. I want you to fly beyond the thrice-ninth land to the thrice-tenth kingdom and bring me the water of death and the water of life.'(See *Foreword: Gods, Rites and Oral Tradition, p.* 10) Whereupon the raven replied to the wolf, 'If, as you promise, you will not harm my baby, I shall do this service for you.' And after uttering these words, the raven took wing and soon disappeared from sight. After three days the raven flew back bearing two phials: in one of them was the water of life and in the other the water of death. She gave them both to the grey wolf. Taking the two phials, the grey wolf tore the young raven in two, sprinkled him with the water of death, and the little raven's body grew together again. Next the wolf sprinkled the bird's feathers with the water of life and the little raven fluttered his wings and began to fly.

The grey wolf then sprinkled Prince Ivan with the water of death, and the murdered man's body grew together again. He sprinkled it also with the water of life, and Prince Ivan stood up and exclaimed, 'Oh, how long have I been sleeping?'

To which the grey wolf replied, 'Indeed, Prince Ivan, you would have slept for an eternity had it not been for me. Your own brothers massacred you and robbed you of Princess Elena the Fair, of the horse with the golden mane and of the firebird. Now hurry back with all possible speed to your own country, for even now your brother Prince Vasili is preparing to marry your beloved Princess Elena the Fair. In order to get there in time, you'd best mount on me, the grey wolf. I will carry you to your destination.'

Prince Ivan sat on the grey wolf and together they sped like lightning to the kingdom of Tsar Vyslav Andronovich. After a short time or a long time, they reached the town. Ivan sprang from the grey wolf and strode into the town. But when he reached the palace he discovered that his brother Prince Vasili had in fact married Princess Elena the Fair and was returning with her from the ceremony to sit at the grand banquet. No sooner did Elena the Fair see Prince Ivan enter the palace than she leapt up from the table and began to kiss his sweet lips, crying out: 'Here is my beloved Prince Ivan. He, and not the scoundrel who sits there at the table, is my bridegroom.'

Then Tsar Vyslav Andronovich rose from his seat. 'Elena the Fair, what do you mean by those words?' he demanded. The princess told him the whole truth about what had happened: how Prince Ivan had won her as well as the horse with the golden mane and the firebird; how the elder brothers had slaughtered Prince Ivan in his sleep; and how they had forced her under threat of death to say that they had achieved all of this.

Tsar Vyslav's anger blazed out at Prince Dimitri and Prince Vasili and he cast them into a dungeon; but Ivan the prince married Princess Elena the Fair and lived with her in such harmony and love that neither of them could bear to be without the other for a single moment.

Know Not

In a certain village, neither far from here nor near, neither high nor low, there dwelt an elderly farmer and his three sons, Grishka, Mishka and Vaniushka. Although Vaniushka was not good at letters and numbers, he was as clever as a fox. He never worked on the farm but spent the whole time lying and dozing by the stove;

he wore his sides off lying there, and would often call out to his brothers with the following words, 'Hey, you old fellows, open the door! I want to take off from here but I *know not* where.' He also sought every opportunity to pester his mother and father: 'Give me now my share of the inheritance; I forego my rights on whatever is left to my brothers.' The old farmer finally gave in to his demands and filled his purse with three hundred roubles. Vaniushka took the money, said farewell to his parents and hurried out of the village.

Arriving in the capital city, he began to wander all around, frequenting the ale houses, spending wildly and gathering all the drunkards around him. The drunkards asked, 'What is your name and who is your father?'

'Truly, my brothers, I *know not*,' he would reply. 'When the priest baptized me and gave me my name, I was young and silly.' For that reason he was nicknamed 'Know Not.'

Know Not wasted his entire fortune in wild living with the drunkards of the city and then began to wonder, poor wretch that he was, how he would survive and avoid utter misery. He approached some cattle dealers and enquired if they needed a workman. 'How much do you want for your wages?' they asked.

Know Not thought to himself that bread stays put, but money takes flight, and answered, 'I don't want to be paid in cash but in kind. Simply allow me to eat my fill and drink until I am sated. I won't ask you for anything, neither need you ask anything of me.' The cattle dealers found this to be an acceptable arrangement, for a hired hand who asked for no money was greatly to their liking. At once they drew up and signed a contract, to make what was said formal and legal.

Know Not was immensely pleased with his free bread and wine. He began to live a merry life, for every day he got completely drunk and fell in a stupor. When he revived and arose he threw himself into the wine again, and spent hour after hour with the bottle in hand, never working. When the dealers ordered him to do some task he would cry angrily, 'Be off with you! Why do you pester me? Have we not agreed in writing that you should let me eat my fill and drink until I am sated, and that I would not ask anything further of you, nor you of me?'

When his term was up the cattle dealers sighed with relief. 'We could not have gone on any longer,' they said. 'We have lost all our bread and wine and will be lucky if he does not sue us in court.'

Having finished with the cattle dealers, Know Not went to the tsar's gardeners and found work as a watchman. His employers quickly concluded an agreement with him on the same terms as the cattle dealers; namely, not to pay him in cash for his labour, but to provide him with as much food and drink as would fill him. Supposedly, Know Not was hired to keep guard over the royal garden, but he caroused by day and by night, and was never sober enough to do an hour's work.

It so happened that one evening all the garden staff were out, and Know Not, for a reason which he *knew not*, decided to uproot the apple trees, the grapevines and the shrubs, and then replant them.

Now the tsar of that region had three daughters. Because it was night the two elder ones had gone to their chambers, but the youngest one, not feeling sleepy, sat among the flowers. She observed Know Not destroying the gardens, exhibiting amazing strength, pulling out old trees by their roots and tossing them over the fence. The following morning the palace gardeners came to work and began to shout and curse: 'What kind of fool are you? Did you not see the person who created such havoc? Who did it?'

'I *know not*!' They laid their hands on him as if he were a criminal and dragged him into the palace before the tsar. Finding himself in the throne room and in the presence of the august tsar, Know Not signed himself with the cross as is prescribed, saluted as he had been taught, made his approach, bowed low as it is enjoined, stood up straight and spoke out boldly, 'Your Majesty! The royal gardens were not laid out in proper fashion and it is no disaster that the old trees were uprooted and flung over the fence! Grant me your permission to put everything in good order, for I can do whatever is necessary.'

The tsar granted his request, and the next night Know Not began to rearrange the royal gardens and put them in good order. He had powerful arms that could lift a tree which twenty men were unable to raise. By morning all the gardens were ready and laid out beautifully. The tsar summoned Know Not before him and poured him a goblet of wine. Know Not took the goblet in his right hand and consumed all of its contents in one draught. Thereupon he took three apples from his cloak and offered them to the three princesses: to the eldest he gave one that was overripe; to the second he gave one that was ripe; and to the youngest, one that was green. The tsar observed this and understood straight away its message for, he realized, his daughters were of age – the eldest should long since have been married, the second one's time had come, and even the youngest had not long to wait.

That same day he called together his dukes, knights and wise counsellors and they all began to ponder how to wed the three princesses. Finally they hit upon a plan: they printed official encyclicals and sent them with messengers to all the surrounding nations, announcing that the tsar wished to give his daughters in marriage and that suitors from every country would be made welcome in his court. And so emperors' sons and kings' sons and mighty heroes made their way to the tsar's court where they sat at an honourable feast. All the suitors ate their fill, drank to satiety, and sat in the hall drunken and happy.

The tsar instructed his daughters to put on garments of many colours, come out of their private quarters and select their future husbands, each according to her heart's desire. Accordingly, the princesses donned garments of many colours, emerged from their chambers to look at the suitors, stood close to them and curtsied politely. These damsels were stately of form and agile of mind; their eyes were as bright as the falcon's, their brows as black as the sable's. Pouring goblets of green and golden wine, they walked along the rows to choose their future husbands. The eldest daughter handed her goblet to the son of an emperor, the second one to the son of a king, but the youngest one carried her goblet up and down the rows, then placed it carefully on a table and spoke these words to her father: 'My sovereign and father, there is no groom for me here.'

'Ah, beloved daughter, before you are gathered the most valiant knights and noble heroes. Is none to your liking?' After the feast the suitors departed.

A second time the tsar called together for a feast the sons of dukes, knights and prosperous merchants. He commanded his youngest daughter to dress in a garment of many colours and choose a husband. She dressed, entered the hall, filled a goblet with green wine, walked up and down the rows of suitors, put the goblet on a table and said, 'My sovereign and father, there is no groom to my liking here.'

'How very fussy you are, my daughter. What kind of man will you ever choose for a groom? Since you are so obstinate, I shall now gather together the sons of burghers, peasants, simpletons, drunkards, jesters, actors and singers. From among them you must choose your husband, whether you like it or not!'

The tsar sent his encyclical to all the towns, villages and hamlets, and at his court there assembled an enormous crowd of burghers, peasants, simpletons, drunkards, jesters, actors and singers. Among them was also Know Not. The princess dressed in a garment of many colours, entered the hall and looked over the humble assembly. She beheld Know Not, who in stature was taller than all of the others. His body was much more massive, too, and his curls fell over his shoulders like threads of pure gold. She came near to him, gave a low curtsy, offered him the goblet of wine and said very politely, 'Drink, my betrothed, you will perform every task.' Know Not received the goblet with his right hand, emptied it in one draught, took the princess by her white hands, kissed her sugar sweet lips and together they came before the tsar himself. Within a few days the tsar ordered all his future sons-in-law to prepare for marriage. They celebrated their weddings and feasted at their feasts, and soon the princess brides began to live happily with their husbands.

Totally preoccupied by these events, the tsar completely forgot to recall his messengers, who had continued on their travels, summoning suitors from foreign lands even further afield. A time came when the messengers reached the Saracen kingdom and they made a proclamation in the public squares and markets about the tsar's quest for suitable sons-in-law. Learning of this, three brave brothers gathered together – valiant warriors, noble heroes, who had journeyed to many countries and conquered many kingdoms.

First the youngest brother set out on his way, accompanied by a vast army. On approaching the tsar's realm and learning that the three princesses were already married, he grew extremely vexed and issued a threatening letter to the tsar, which read: 'I have journeyed from the Saracen kingdom with peaceful motives, to woo your daughters, and to that end I have crossed many lands and provinces. Now I have been informed that you have given your daughters in marriage and failed to recall your messengers, therefore I demand compensation for the damage and costs that I have incurred. If you do not pay me, I shall burn your entire city to the ground, slaughter its population and put you yourself, in spite of your great age, to a hideous death.'

The tsar became very alarmed and said to his sons-in-law, 'My beloved children, what shall we do?' With one voice the emperor's son and the king's son replied, 'We do not fear this threat; we shall ourselves wage battle against this Saracen. Summon, O father, a host of troops and the mounted warriors as well.' Eventually a great legion of soldiers was assembled. The emperor's son led the infantry regiments and the king's son commanded the mounted troops. Together they went out to the open field, looked upon the valiant Saracen, that noble hero, and his vast army, and took fright, fleeing to their country estates beyond the thick forests and swampy marshes, so that no one could detect a trace of them. Their regiments and troops were left leaderless, helpless and in terror of the judgement day.

Meanwhile, Know Not lay by the stove and his noble heart boiled with rage. Turning to the princess, he said, 'My beloved wife, let us go to the country, for at any moment the city may be burned, the people slaughtered and your own father, the tsar, taken captive. This affair is none of our doing, we are not responsible for this catastrophe.'

'Certainly not,' answered the tsar's daughter. 'Better that I die than leave my mother and father in their hour of greatest need.' She bade Know Not farewell and went out to her father on the terrace. The tsar remained motionless on the terrace looking through a telescope at the field of battle.

Know Not, however, did not escape to the country like his brothers-in-law. He dressed as a simple peasant, placed a cap on his head, donned a caftan and mittens, and went through the city unrecognized. He climbed a high hill at the edge of the city, shouted a heroic shout and whistled a warlike whistle. Within seconds there galloped from the open field a brave steed bearing a full suit of armour. From his mouth streamed fiery flames, from his ears rolled curls of smoke and from his snorting nostrils flew brilliant sparks. The horse's tail was three cubits long and his mane reached to his hoofs. Coming up to the horse, the peasant Know Not decked it out with saddlecloths, blankets and a Moroccan saddle. He fastened the twelve saddle girths and laid the thirteenth over the animal's chest. These girths were of white silk, the buckles of red gold and the clamps of steel – not so much for appearance as for heroic strength: for silk does not tear, steel does not bend and red gold does not rust in the ground. As for himself, Know Not was attired in full battle accessories – iron mail, a steel shield, a long spear, a battle mace and a sharp sword. He leapt on to his good steed and lashed his slender flanks, cutting the horse's flesh to the white bone. The gallant steed flew into a rage and raised himself above Moist Mother Earth, higher than the tallest trees, just short of the swiftly moving clouds. Each leap he made was thirty feet high. From beneath his mighty hoofs enormous mounds of earth were dug up, underground springs gushed high into the air, the water in the lakes surged back and forth, mixing with the yellow sand, and the trees in the forest shook and bent low to the ground.

Know Not shouted his heroic shout, whistled his warlike whistle, and the ferocious beasts on chains began to roar, the nightingales in the gardens began to sing, and the serpents and adders began to hiss. Such was Know Not's fabulous ride. He sallied forth past the tsar's palace, in front of its entrance, and cried out, 'Greetings, august sovereign and all your royal attendants!' He leapt over the white stone walls, over the corner turrets and into the field where the terrified army and mounted troops stood transfixed. To them he cried aloud, 'Greetings, my warriors, where are your brave leaders?' And there in the open field he laid eyes on the valiant Saracen, the noble hero, galloping on his good steed, circling the plain like an eagle, striking fear into the tsar's host. Know Not shouted again, this time in a shrill voice like a silver trumpet, and the two champions rode toward each other, raising their iron maces that each weighed two thousand pounds.

When they struck at each other, the impact of mail on mail was like a mountain avalanche. Their maces clashed and broke, only the staffs remained in their hands. Once again they withdrew a great distance from each other in the open field, wheeled their brave horses around and charged toward each other at lightning speed. They each thrust their spears at one another; the spears bent to the handles but could not pierce the mail. But now the Saracen champion faltered in his saddle.

Yet again they rode apart in the open field, and at the third encounter, they struck each other with their sharp swords and Know Not knocked the valiant Saracen from his saddle onto Moist Mother Earth. The light in the eyes of the fallen champion grew dim; from his mouth and nose blood began to flow. Know Not jumped down from his steed, forced the enemy to Moist Mother Earth, drew a mighty dagger from his pocket, a knife of steel that weighed sixty pounds, slit open the multi-coloured raiment of the Saracen knight, bared his white breast, searched for his fiery heart, shed his hot blood and destroyed his heroic strength. Then he sliced off the turbulent head, raised it high on his spear and shouted in a triumphant voice, 'Oh my dear friends, brave brothers-in-law! Come out, come out of the thick forests; draw near from the swampy marshes and take charge of your soldiers and mounted troops. They are all safe and sound.'

After this Know Not turned his bold steed around. The horse flew like the bright falcon; its feet soared high in the sky. Soon he approached the city where he was met by the tsar, the royal attendants and Know Not's own wife. They all raced down from the palace's terrace to express their gratitude. But Know Not threw a scarf over his face. 'No one must recognize me,' he said to himself.

'Valiant young knight! Where are you from, who is your father and what good fortune has sent you to preserve us from our enemies? I *know not* what gifts to give you; I *know not* what rewards or honours. You are the palace's most welcome guest.' The disguised Know Not replied, 'Neither your bread shall I eat, nor your words shall I heed.' He then rode to the outskirts of the city into the green thicket, removed the Moroccan saddle from his steed and let him roam freely; he took off his steel armour, the iron coat of mail, put all the accessories away temporarily in a secret hiding place and went home to his wife. When he arrived at his dwelling, he put on his old clothes and lay down to sleep by the stove.

'Ah, Know Not, dear husband! You *know not*, for you have not yet heard. A brave young hero appeared from the green thicket and shouted in so mighty a voice that all who heard it were struck with fear. On his noble steed he leapt over these white stone walls and over the corner turrets into the open field where stood the tsar's infantry and mounted troops, who scarcely had a moment to make room for him. At the sound of a loud trumpet the Saracen champion arose and turned his horse to attack him. They rode toward each other and clashed together like thunder clouds; their maces struck and broke, only the staffs remained in their hands. They clashed a second time, thrust their spears together but the spears bent like serpents to their handles. Yet a third time did they meet, this time with swords in their hands. But the Saracen collapsed onto Moist Mother Earth, the young warrior leapt from the saddle onto his mighty chest, slit open his white body, searched for his fiery heart, shed his hot blood and sliced the turbulent head from the enemy's shoulders. This head he then raised aloft on his spear and rode into the open field.'

'Ah, you foolish woman. You *know nothing*, neither the ways of men nor the ways of beasts in the dark forest. There are no such heroes in the white world.'

Meanwhile, the tsar's sons-in-law came out of the woods and the thickets, assembled in the open field, gathered together their host of soldiers and mounted troops, and led them into the city. The bells tolled, the army bands beat their drums, sounded their trumpets and sang their songs. The tsar commanded that the gates be opened to them and that their entry be in triumph. All of the men-at-arms were treated to wine in the city's taverns and inns; all of the citizens feasted with joy. This recreation lasted six whole weeks, everyone ate and drank their fill; all were drunken and merry. Only Know Not, the tsar's youngest son-in-law, was unwelcome at the celebrations, for none knew of his part in the proceedings or of the great load that he had carried.

One day he said to his wife, 'My beloved wife, unloved of her father, go and ask the tsar for a cup of green wine for me to drink and a piece of ham for me to eat.'

The princess went to the palace and, approaching her father, curtsied low, looked at him straight in the eye and boldly uttered these words: 'My sovereign and father, I beg a favour of you. Give my husband and your son-in-law, Know Not, a cup of green wine to drink and a piece of ham to eat.'

'Water does not flow under a resting stone. Your husband and my son-in-law fled like a coward to the country in our distress and he became a great embarrassment for all. And now with the triumphant conquest of our enemy he has come back to his dwelling and rests by the stove. Alas, my beloved daughter! If only you had married a heroic warrior who would cheerfully have entered into battle to defeat the Saracen host! Then my heart would have rejoiced and you would have been saved the insult. Be that as it may, we must leave things as they are and your husband must be satisfied with the particles that remain when the feast is over.'

'Not everyone is like your elder sons-in-law who hid in the dark woods at the hour of battle and then rushed back at the moment of another's conquest, to drink and to be merry. Is it fair that my husband and I should lick the platters after them?'

At the same time as the princess made her reproach, a swift-footed envoy arrived in the Saracen kingdom. Immediately he sought out the other two mighty heroes and described the woeful catastrophe. 'A brave warrior sallied forth,' he said, 'and decapitated your brother. His mutilated body still lies on the open field; his hot blood was shed; and the survivors of his vast army were taken captive.' The two champions became furious with anger. They quickly mounted their noble horses, put on their steel armour and their coats of iron mail, and took up their warlike arms – the steel swords, battle maces of iron, razor-sharp sabres and long spears – and headed off to seek revenge. Ahead of them they despatched a messenger to the tsar bearing a threatening letter with the following words: 'Deliver the knight who shed the innocent blood of our beloved brother. If you do not, we shall harvest all of your troops with our swords, light up the heavens with flames that will burn your city, take your people captive and subject you to a hideous death, in spite of your great age.' The messenger entered the palace and delivered this letter to the tsar who took it, broke its seal and read it trembling. His legs collapsed under him, his white hands shook and the sight of his bright eyes was blurred, for burning tears flowed from them.

The tsar pondered the matter gravely and then sent runners out in all directions to summon his counsellors, generals, senior officers and other eye-witnesses, both humble and great, to question them about the brave hero who had slaughtered the Saracen warrior. But the man was *not known* to anyone: the higher-ranking officers referred the matter to the middle-ranking officers; the middle-ranking officers referred it to the lower-ranking officers; and they in turn to the citizens of the kingdom. There was no answer. So the tsar was obliged to send the courier back to the Saracens with the message that he was *not known*.

Totally dissatisfied with what seemed to them to be a ruse, the two Saracen brothers sallied forth, leaving a trail of destruction behind them: towns, villages and hamlets were burnt to the ground. Meanwhile Know Not rested by the stove at home, his fiery heart boiling with rage, and he spoke these words to his wife: 'My beloved wife, unloved of her father, let us repair to the country, for life here has become unbearable.'

'Certainly not,' answered the tsar's daughter. 'Better that I die than leave my mother and father in their hour of greatest need.'

Know Not raised himself up and, sighing deeply, warned the princess, 'If your father is killed, you will not remain alive either. Farewell, my beloved wife.' He then put on peasant clothes, placed a cap on his head, took a stick in his hand, went outside and looked about, making certain that he was not seen by anyone. But in fact the tsar happened to see him from the terrace. 'What is wrong with this simpleton?' he thought. 'He wants to escape like a coward but it does not occur to him if things go badly for us every member of our family will be hunted down!'

Beside him stood the other two sons-in-law who were trying to think of a way in which they could demonstrate their courage. 'Our sovereign and father, assemble a host of infantrymen and the mounted troops so we can be of assistance in your hour of need.'

Thereupon the tsar gathered together an enormous army and organized regiments. His sons-in-law called for their own soldiers and they marched forward to the field of battle. The Saracen knights charged headlong onto these front line divisions, smote them brutally with their swords and trampled a great multitude with their mighty steeds. Rivers of blood gushed forth and the demented cry of the wounded could be heard for miles. Know Not also heard them; he rushed to the aid of the injured, climbed a high hill, shouted the shout of a hero and whistled a mighty whistle. At this signal his heroic steed came running from the open field, but as he ran he accidentally stumbled. 'Why, you carcass for wolves, you bag of weeds,' cried Know Not, 'for what reason did you stumble? Do you smell the scent of misfortune?'

'There will be blood spilt on both the horse and the master,' prophesied the good steed. Know Not set about preparing his horse for battle. He placed on him his bridle, saddlecloths, blankets and the Moroccan saddle. He tightened the twelve saddle girths, while the thirteenth he placed on the animal's chest. All the girths were of white Persian silk, the buckles of red Arabian gold, the clasps of steel from far-off places, not for the purposes of beauty, but for heroic strength. For silk does not tear, steel does not bend and red gold does not rust.

Having equipped his steed, he then began to prepare himself. He put on his knight's garment with steel armour, arming himself with the steel shield and the battle mace of iron. He attached the large, stout spear to his legs, the razor-sharp sabre to his waist and the steel sword behind him.

Know Not then mounted his heroic steed, placed his nimble feet into the silver stirrups, took up a silken rider's whip and lashed his horse on his slender flanks, searing his skin. The beast flew into a rage and raised himself above Moist Mother Earth, higher than the tallest trees, just short of the swiftly moving clouds. He leapt from mountain to mountain, straddling rivers and lakes with his legs, sweeping deep marshes with his tail. A flame sprang out of his mouth, sparks flew from his nostrils, curling smoke wafted from his ears, beneath his hoofs enormous clumps of earth were dug up and underground springs gushed forth. When Know Not shouted his heroic shout and whistled his warlike whistle, the water in the lakes burst forth, mixing with the yellow sand, and the ancient oaks quivered, bending their tops to the ground.

In the open field one of the Saracen knights emerged, seated on his horse, solid as a haystack. His steed flew like a falcon and did not touch Moist Mother Earth.

'Insolent youth, I will consume you whole!' he boasted.

As the two champions approached each other, Know Not's horse said, 'Now, my master, lower your head over my mane and perhaps you will be saved.' No sooner had Know Not done this than the Saracen hero let fly with his sword, injuring Know Not's left arm and slicing off the bold steed's left ear. At once Know Not hurled his spear into the Saracen knight's chest just below the neck and struck him down like an ear of corn. The Saracen fell on Moist Mother Earth and lay there wallowing in his hot blood. At the sight of this crushing defeat, the third brother and the enemy troops fled from sight.

Soon afterwards the tsar's infantrymen and mounted troops came forward and entered the city walls behind Know Not and his steed. At the tsar's palace Know Not's voice was heard to exclaim: 'My faithful people, do not let me die in vain, bandage my left arm to stop the flow of blood!' All of the tsar's attendants hastened down from the terrace, including the princess, Know Not's wife, who was the first to reach him. She bound his bleeding wound with her own handkerchief but she did not recognize him as her husband because he was wiping the sweat from his brow, and so concealing his face.

Having recovered sufficiently, Know Not rode to his dwelling, left his steed untied outside, entered the hall, fell on the floor and covered his face with his hand. The tsar was none the wiser. He stood on the terrace and watched his two elder sons-in-law finish off the remnants of the enemy army. Meanwhile Know Not's wife approached her home and immediately saw the hero's steed with all its battle accessories at the entrance, and the hero himself lying in the hall. She hurried back to her father and told him everything. In haste the tsar went with his attendants to his daughter's home, opened the door, fell on his knees and said very gently, 'Tell me, good knight, who is your family and from which tribe are you? What is your name and that of your father?'

'Ah, my sovereign and God-given father, do you not recognize me? You have always called me a simpleton.' At that everyone realized who he was and paid him due honour as a mighty hero. As soon as they heard of this triumph, the elder sons-in-law packed up their belongings and took their wives back to their homes. Know Not soon recovered from his wounds, drank green wine and invited everyone to an honourable feast. After the tsar's death he ascended the throne and his life was long and happy.

Ivan and Ivan, the Soldier's Sons

In a certain kingdom, in a certain land, there once dwelt a peasant. The time came when he was called to serve as a soldier, so he had to leave his lovely wife, who was expecting their first child. As he bade her farewell, he said, 'Hear me well, good woman: live respectably, do not scorn good people nor give cause for ridicule. Do not permit our little house to fall into chaos but care for it prudently and await my return. With the help of God I may be dismissed and come back soon. Nevertheless, here are fifty roubles for you. This is money for our child. Whether it be a little son or a daughter, keep it until he or she comes of age. If you have a daughter this will be her dowry for the bridegroom that God provides; but if you give birth to a son, I fear this amount will be little help to him when he grows up.' Then he took leave of his wife and went to the infantry barracks to which he was assigned.

Three months passed and his wife gave birth to twin sons. She named both of them Ivan. In time the youngsters began to grow; like wheat dough leavened with yeast they shot up broad and tall. At ten years of age their mother sent them off to begin their education and very quickly they learned to read and write. So bright were they that all the noblemen's and merchants' sons envied them. In fact, no one could recite aloud, create prose or answer questions as well as they. Because they could not hold a candle to Ivan and Ivan, the other boys bullied and pinched them every day.

One of the brothers said to the other, 'How long will they torment and beat us? Our poor mother will never to able to make us enough clothes or buy us enough caps, for whatever we wear our fellow students tear to shreds. Let us teach them a lesson.' So they agreed to defend themselves appropriately. The following day, as usual, the noblemen's and merchants' sons began to bully them, but instead of bearing it like martyrs, the brothers responded in like fashion. They blackened the eye of one, dislocated the hand of another and smashed the ear of a third.

Each and every aggressor was beaten black and blue. Their cries and groans were heard all around the school yard. Immediately the guards came, arrested the two Ivans and threw them into prison. The whole episode was even brought to the ears of the tsar himself, who called for the youths, interrogated them thoroughly, and finally pardoned them and ordered their release. 'They are innocent,' he said. 'God has punished those who instigated the fight.'

When the two boys grew up they asked their mother, 'Mother dear, did not our father the soldier leave us some money? If so, let us have it, for we wish to go to the fair in town and purchase two good horses, one for each of us.' Their mother gave them the fifty roubles, twenty-five to each brother, and said, 'Hear me well, my children. As you journey to town make certain that you bow to every person whose path you cross.'

'Very well, dear mother, we shall not forget,' said the two Ivans.

So the brothers set off for town and went to the horse market at the fair. They examined all the steeds carefully, but although there were many, not one was a good enough mount for the two brothers. One Ivan then said to the other, 'Let us take a walk to the other end of the square for I can see that a great crowd is assembling there. Something unusual must be happening.' They made their way through the jostling crowd and there spotted two spirited horses attached to stout oaken posts with iron clamps; one with six clamps, the other with twelve. The beasts were pulling furiously at their chains, gnawing their bits and digging into the ground with their hoofs. It was impossible for anyone to get near them. 'How much do these mares cost?' asked Ivan the soldier's son.

'Don't stick your nose into this one, my friend,' answered the owner. 'Mares like these are not for the likes of you. Forget it.'

'What are you talking about? How do you know what my likes are? I may well be in a position to buy them, only first I must look at their teeth.'

'Go right ahead, be my guest, and look closely – only not too closely because you might well lose your turbulent head,' chuckled the owner. One of the brothers then approached one of the horses, that which was fastened with six clamps, while his brother went to inspect the horse that was held by twelve. They made several brave attempts to look at the horses' teeth, but the task seemed impossible. The mares rose up on their hind legs, pawed the air and snorted viciously. The brothers then decided to strike the beasts in the breast with their knees. At this the chains which held the horses snapped like biscuits and the mares flew up in the air to a height of ten yards then fell down with their legs uppermost. 'So,' cried the brothers, 'why do you boast about such ponies? We wouldn't even accept animals like these as a gift.'

The angry mares had galloped clear out of town and sped swiftly over the open fields. 'What mighty horses are these,' gasped the crowd, amazed at this exhibition of strength. The horse dealer was almost reduced to tears at the loss of his horses. No one had the courage to come near to them; no one knew how to catch them.

The two Ivans felt very sorry for the owner, so they went out into the open field, shouted out with a thunderous voice and whistled lustily. The mares returned to their place in the square and stood quietly as if rooted to the spot. The two brothers placed the iron chains upon them again, led them to the oaken posts and bound them firmly. Then they set off for home.

As they went along the road they met an old, grey-bearded man, but forgetting what their mother had told them, they passed him by without bowing to him. A little later, one of the brothers realized their error and cried, 'Oh brother Ivan, look what we've done! We completely forgot to give that old man a bow. Let us run back and make our bow to him.' They ran after the old grey-beard, removed their caps, bowed low to the waist and said apologetically, 'Forgive us, grandfather, for neglecting to greet you as we passed by. Our mother advised us strictly to make an obeisance to every person whose path we cross.'

'I thank you, my good lads. Where is God leading you?'

'We visited the town fair in order to buy two horses, one for each of us, but there was none there that suited us.'

'How could that be? Suppose now that I were to present both of you with a little nag each?'

'Ah, grandfather, if you were to do that, we would always pray to God for you.'

'Well, come along with me.' The old man led them to an enormous mountain, opened two cast iron doors and produced two horses of heroic breed.

'Here, take your horses, my young men, and God speed you on your journey. Look after them and may they bring you enjoyment and good fortune.' The brothers expressed their profound gratitude, bowed low to him again, mounted the steeds and galloped homeward. Reaching the yard, they tethered the horses to a post and entered the house.

'Well, my dear children,' asked their mother, 'did you buy yourselves a couple of horses?'

'We did not buy them with our roubles, but received them as a gift.'

'Where have you left them?'

'In the front yard of our house. Why do you ask?'

'O my children, someone might steal them! Look to see if anyone has taken them away!'

'That would be impossible, mother. No one could ever get near to these heroic beasts; no one could ever lead them.' The mother stepped outside to the yard, looked at the horses and burst into tears.

'Ah, my dear sons,' she moaned, 'you will surely never be my strength or support.'

The following day the two Ivans asked permission of their mother to go into the town and buy two swords – one for each of them. 'Go, my dear sons,' she said.

They made ready and went to the smithy. 'Make us each a sturdy sword,' they said to the master smith.

'Why should I make them when they are already at hand?' said the smith. 'Take whichever ones you like best.'

'No, my friend; we require swords that weigh four hundred pounds each!'

'What in the world are you talking about?' scoffed the smith. 'Who could wield an instrument like that? Which forge could forge them? No, my lads, such swords simply do not exist.' Disappointed, the two youths hung their heads and slowly went back to the house. As they were on their way, sullen and in no mood to talk, they met again the same old grey-bearded man.

'Greetings, my young friends!' he called.

'Good day to you, grandfather,' they replied unenthusiastically.

'Where have you come from?'

'We were at the smith's in town looking for two Damascus blades – one for each of us – but there were none that suited our purposes.'

'That's most unfortunate. Suppose now I were to give each one of you a sword. What would you say?'

'O dear grandfather, if you were to do that, we would always pray to God for you.' The old beard led them to the same enormous mountain, opened the cast iron doors and drew out two swords fit for heroes. The brothers took them, thanked the old man and bowed respectfully. Their grateful hearts were full of joy.

When they returned to their home, their mother asked, 'Well, my sons, have you bought yourselves each a sword?'

'We did not buy them with our roubles, but received them as a gift.'

'And what have you done with them?'

'We have placed them upright beside the front door of the house. Why do you ask?'

'Beware, for somebody might come and take them away.'

'That would be impossible, dear mother. Swords of this size and weight cannot be lifted up, let alone carried away.'

The mother went out of the front door and looked about. The two massive grey swords were leaning upright against the wall. In fact, the house was barely able to bear the weight of them. She burst into tears and moaned, 'Ah, my dear sons, you will surely never be my strength or support.'

The following morning, the two Ivans, sons of the soldier, saddled their good horses, took up their mighty blades, came into the house, prayed to God and took leave of the mother who had borne them. 'Bestow on us your blessing, dear mother, for a long road lies before us,' they said.

'Let my unshakeable maternal blessing be upon you both, my sons,' she said. 'Go in God's name, show yourselves, and see the world. Offend none without cause, and do not yield to evil ways.'

'Have no fear, dear mother. We have this motto: "When I eat I don't whistle, and when I bite I don't let go."' Then the good youths mounted their steeds and set off.

After they had journeyed a short way or a long way (for with speed is a tale spun, but slowly is a deed full done) they came at last to a crossroad where two oaken columns stood. On one was inscribed the following text: 'He who goes to the right will become a tsar'; while on the other column was written, 'He who goes to the left will be killed.' The brothers halted, read the lines on the column carefully, and pondered deeply: 'Which path shall we take? If both take the right there will neither be honour nor glory enough for the heroic strength and youthful prowess of us both. On the other hand, nobody wants to go to the left and die.' The choice was extremely difficult, but it had to be made. So one brother said to the other, 'See now, dear brother, my strength is greater than yours; permit me to go to the left and see what could possibly cause my death. You go to the right; perhaps God will help you and make you a tsar.' They then bid each other farewell, exchanged handkerchiefs, and made a solemn pact – each was to go his own way, place posts along the road, and inscribe facts about himself on these posts as a mark and guide. Moreover, they pledged that every morning each of them would wipe his face with his brother's handkerchief, and if one of them should see blood appearing on the cloth, it would mean that his brother had had a tragic end, and in such a calamity he was to set out in search of the body.

The good youths parted ways. The one who turned his horse to the right came to a magnificent kingdom wherein dwelt a tsar, his queen and their daughter, the thrice beautiful Nastasia. When the tsar set his eyes on Ivan, the soldier's son, he loved him for his knightly valour, and without giving any time for a second thought, gave him his daughter to wed. Ivan himself was given the title of prince and was made ruler over the whole kingdom. He enjoyed a very happy life, loved his wife dearly, exercised proper law and order over his kingdom and entertained himself with the pleasures of the hunt.

One day Prince Ivan made preparations to go hunting. As he began to place the bridle on his horse he discovered two phials sewn up in the saddle: one contained the water of death and the other the water of life.[2] The prince examined these phials and put them back into the saddle. 'I shall keep them for an hour of danger,' he thought. 'One day they may serve a useful purpose.'

Meanwhile, what had befallen the other Ivan? Having taken the road to the left he rode on day and night without rest. One month, a second month, and even a third month passed, until he found himself in an unknown kingdom and wearily dismounted in the centre of its capital. In this place there was great mourning, the buildings were draped with black cloth and the people drifted about as if they were half asleep. He rented simple quarters at the home of a poor old woman and began to question her: 'Tell me, grandmother,' he asked, 'why are all the people in this realm so full of grief, and why are all the buildings covered in black cloth?'

2.   See Foreword: Gods, Rites and Oral Tradition, p. 10

'Alas, good youth,' the old woman lamented, 'a heavy sorrow weighs upon us. Every day a twelve-headed serpent comes out of the blue sea, from behind a grey rock, and devours a man or woman. Now has come the turn of the tsar's own family. He has three very beautiful daughters and at this very moment the eldest is being escorted to the seashore to be sacrificed to the monster.'

Ivan, the soldier's son, leapt on to his brave horse and raced like lightning to the blue sea, to the grey rock. There on the sandy shore stood the thrice-beautiful princess, held in an iron chain. Seeing the hero, she called out to him, 'Depart from this place, good youth. Very soon the twelve-headed serpent will appear and I shall meet my end. If you remain here any longer, you too will perish, for the cruel serpent will swallow you whole.'

'Have no fear, my lovely damsel,' he replied, 'if he swallows me whole he may meet his own doom by suffocation.'

The mighty Ivan went up to her, pulled at the chain with his powerful hand, and tore it into shreds as if it were a rotten rope. Then he uprooted oaks and pine trees and piled them into an enormous pyre all around the grey rock. He lit the fire and then returned to the damsel and laid his head on her knee.

'Now pick in my hair for lice while I rest; but do not become so absorbed in this task as to neglect watching the sea. As soon as a cloud arises and the wind begins to blow fiercely, and the sea to surge and roar, awaken me, my princess.' Then he fell into a deep sleep while the beautiful damsel followed his instructions. She picked his hair, but always kept an eagle's eye trained on the sea. Suddenly a cloud came over the horizon, the wind began to blow fiercely, the sea surged and roared. The ugly serpent came forth from the blue depths and raised itself in the air as high as the highest mountain.

The princess tried to rouse Ivan the soldier's son. She shook him time and again but it was no use, he would not wake up. Then she burst into a flood of tears and when her burning teardrops fell on the hero's cheeks he immediately arose and ran to his steed. As it plunged and reared the brave beast had ploughed up half a fathom of earth with his hoofs.

The twelve-headed serpent rushed straight at Ivan belching forth tongues of red fire. It gazed upon the hero in disdain and warned him in a loud voice, 'Indeed you are brave and strong, my handsome youth, but your hour has come; prepare to meet your death. The place where you stand is mine. Make your farewells to the white world and rush headlong into my throat of your own accord – it will be less painful that way.'

'You are a liar, accursed dragon,' answered Ivan. 'Surrender now; you cannot swallow me, for you will surely choke to death.'

Then they fell to mortal combat. The soldier's son wielded his sharp sword so deftly and sturdily that it grew red hot – too hot, in fact, for him to hold in his hand. He cried out to the princess, 'Save me, beautiful damsel. Take out your fair handkerchief, dip it into the blue sea, and give it to me to wrap around my sword.'

At once the princess moistened her handkerchief in the sea and gave it to the valiant fighter. Ivan wrapped it around his sword and resumed the fierce combat against the serpent. But no matter how hard he tried, he could not overpower the monster with his sword. Turning to the burning pyre, he seized a red-hot pine-brand and thrust its burning stump into the serpent's eye. Bearing his sharp sword he took a mighty swing, hewing off all twelve heads. Then he lifted up the grey rock and put the heads under it, and threw the body into the sea. He returned home to the old woman, ate and drank his fill, lay down to rest, and slept peacefully for thrice four-and-twenty hours.

In the meantime, the tsar summoned his water bearer and said to him, 'Go to the seashore and gather up my daughter's remains, if there be any.'

The water bearer drove down to the seashore in a cart, and behold, the princess was alive and unhurt. He lifted her into his cart and headed, not for the palace, but into a dense forest – far into the forest he took her. There he brought out a dagger from his belt and began to sharpen it.

'What do you mean to do?' asked the terrified damsel.

'I am sharpening my dagger to slit your throat,' replied the evil water bearer.

'Do not murder me! What harm have I done you?' she implored.

'If you tell your father, the tsar, that it was I who slew the serpent and saved you, I shall have mercy on your life,' the man said. He filled her heart with terror, and having no other choice, she promised to speak according to his wishes. They went to the palace. When the tsar saw that she was alive and unhurt, he was pleased beyond telling and wished to reward the water bearer, so he presented him with many honours and riches.

When Ivan eventually awoke he called the old woman, gave her some money, and asked of her, 'Grandmother, would you go to the market, purchase what things are necessary, and listen to what the townspeople are saying among themselves? Find out the latest news and let me know immediately.'

The old woman went to the market and bought food and drink. She listened to the talk of the town, returned to her home and reported to Ivan: 'This is what I heard the townspeople saying among themselves: there was a great banquet at the tsar's palace: princes, ambassadors, nobles and heroes were seated at the table. Suddenly an iron arrow shot through the window and fell in the middle of the hall. Attached to that arrow was a letter from another twelve-headed serpent which read: "Send me your second daughter otherwise I shall burn down your entire kingdom and it will be nothing but ashes." Even now they are taking the poor damsel down to the blue sea, to the grey rock.'

At once Ivan saddled his good steed, leapt up on his back, and raced like lightning to the shore. The princess saw him and said, 'What brings you here, young man? Now it is my turn to be offered in sacrifice to the monster and to shed my innocent blood. Depart, or else you too will be devoured.'

'Have no fear, beautiful damsel,' said Ivan. 'God will save you.' No sooner had he uttered these words than the evil serpent flew up to him. Tongues of fire were issuing from his mouth and nostrils, and he prepared to turn the soldier's son into a cinder. The brave hero attacked him with his sharp sword and cut off all of his twelve heads. These he put under the grey rock, threw the rest of the body into the sea, returned home, ate and drank his fill, and again lay down to sleep for thrice four-and-twenty hours.

The same water bearer went down to the seashore to find what was left of the princess. He saw that she was alive and unhurt, lifted her into his cart, drove into the dense forest, and set about sharpening his knife.

The princess asked him, 'Why are you sharpening your knife?'

Because I mean to cut your white throat,' he said. 'But if you promise to tell your father, the tsar, that I saved you, I will have mercy on your life.' The terrified princess took an oath to this effect, and the water bearer took her to the palace. The tsar was pleased beyond telling and bestowed more honours and riches on the water bearer.

Ivan eventually awoke and asked the old woman, his landlady, to go to the market, buy the necessary provisions, and listen to the latest news of the townspeople. Upon returning, she reported the following: 'Yet a third dragon has appeared. He sent the tsar a letter insisting under threat that the youngest princess be sent to him for sacrifice.'

The soldier's son saddled his good steed, leapt upon his back, and raced like lightning to the shore. There on the sand stood the beautiful princess, fettered to the rock with an iron chain. The mighty champion pulled at the chain with his powerful hand and tore it into shreds, as if it were a rotten rope. Then he came up to the beautiful damsel, laid his head on her knees, and said to her, 'Now pick in my hair for lice while I rest, but do not become so absorbed in this task as to neglect watching the sea. As soon as a cloud arises and the wind begins to blow fiercely, and the sea to surge and roar, awaken me, my princess.'

She picked in his hair, but always kept an eagle eye trained on the sea. Suddenly a cloud arose over the horizon, the wind began to blow fiercely, the sea surged and roared. The ugly serpent came forth from the blue depths and raised itself in the air. The princess tried to rouse Ivan. She shook him time and again, but it was no use, he would not wake up. Then she burst into a flood of tears and when her burning teardrops fell on the hero's cheeks, he immediately arose, ran to his steed and discovered that the brave beast had already ploughed up half a fathom of earth with his hoofs.

The twelve-headed serpent rushed straight at him, belching forth tongues of red fire. It gazed upon the hero in disdain and warned him in a loud voice, 'Indeed you are brave and strong, my handsome youth, but the hour has come. Prepare to meet your death. I shall chew on your every last bone.'

'You are a liar, accursed dragon,' answered Ivan. 'Surrender now; you cannot chew my bones, for you will surely choke on them.' Then they fell to mortal combat. The soldier's son wielded his sharp sword so deftly and sturdily that it grew red hot – too hot, in fact, for him to hold in his hand. He cried out to the princess, 'Save me, beautiful damsel. Take out your fair handkerchief, dip it into the blue sea, and give it to me to wrap around my sword.'

At once the princess moistened her handkerchief in the sea and gave it to the valiant fighter who wrapped it around his sword. In less time than it takes for a hawk to pounce on a field-mouse, Ivan slew the evil serpent, hacked off all twelve heads, put them under the grey rock, threw its body into the sea, returned home to the old woman, ate and drank his fill, lay down to rest, and slept for thrice four-and-twenty hours.

Once more the tsar sent the water bearer to the seashore to recover whatever was left of the princess. The water bearer went down to the blue sea, to the grey rock, and behold, he found her alive and unhurt. He placed her in his cart and drove her into the dense forest – far into the forest he took her – and there he brought out a dagger from his belt and began to sharpen it.

'What do you mean to do?' asked the terrified damsel.

'I am sharpening my dagger to slit your throat,' replied the evil water bearer.

'Do not murder me! What harm have I done you?' she implored.

'If you tell your father, the tsar, that it was I who slew the serpent and saved you, I shall have mercy on your life.' He filled her heart with terror, and having no other choice, she promised to speak according to his wishes.

Now this daughter was the tsar's favourite, and when he saw that she was alive and unhurt, he was even more overjoyed than before, and as a reward to the water bearer, he gave him this youngest daughter to wed. Word of the betrothal spread rapidly around the kingdom and even reached the ears of Ivan the soldier's son. On the day that the marriage was being celebrated at the palace, Ivan dressed in his best attire and joined the feast.

The tsar had prepared a splendid banquet; the guests were eating and drinking and entertaining themselves with games and amusements. When she looked upon Ivan at the entrance, the youngest princess recognized her costly handkerchief wrapped around his mighty sword and leapt up from her seat. She took Ivan by his hand and presented him to her father, saying, 'My dear father and sovereign lord, behold, this is the man who saved your daughters from the cruel serpent and from violent death. The only thing that your water bearer could do was to sharpen his dagger and say, "I am sharpening my dagger to slit your throat."'

The tsar began to boil with rage. He gave orders for the deceitful water bearer to be hanged at once and married the princess to Ivan the soldier's son. There was great festivity, the young couple lived very happily together and their life was long and prosperous.

Meanwhile, hardly had three days elapsed, when new events befell the other brother, Prince Ivan. He went out with a hunting party one day and startled a swift-footed stag. The prince dug his spurs into his horse's flanks and chased after that stag. On and on he sped, until Ivan found himself in a broad meadow where the stag simply disappeared from before his eyes. Prince Ivan looked about him and pondered, 'Which way should I now go?'

Then he spotted a small stream flowing in the meadow, and on the water two grey ducks were swimming. He took aim at them and killed the pair of ducks, then he dragged them out of the water, put them into a sack, and continued further into the meadow. He went on and on until he came across a white stone palace. Dismounting from his steed and tethering it to a post, he entered its chambers. To his astonishment, the prince realized that every chamber was empty. There was not a living soul in the palace. However, in one room there was a stove with its fire burning, a large frying pan stood on the hearth, and the table was already laid with plates, glasses, forks and knives. Prince Ivan brought out the ducks from his sack, cleaned and dressed them, put them in the pan and the pan in the oven. When the ducks were cooked to a turn, he placed them on the table and began to carve and eat them.

Suddenly out of nowhere a beautiful damsel appeared before him – of a loveliness that is only sung about in songs or written about with pens – and said to him, 'Bread and salt to the welcome guest, Ivan the prince.'

'By your leave, gracious damsel, please partake of this food with me,' said Ivan.

'I would like to sit down with you, but I am afraid. You have an enchanted horse.'

'Not at all, my lovely maiden, you have made a mistake. My magic horse is at home. This one that I am riding today is only an ordinary one, like any other.' As soon as the beautiful lady heard this she began to swell up and swell up and turned into a vicious lioness. She opened wide her jaws and swallowed up Prince Ivan whole. This was not an ordinary damsel, but the very sister of the serpents that had been slain by Ivan the hero.

Around the same time it happened that Ivan the soldier's son stopped and called his brother to mind. Drawing from his pocket the handkerchief given him by his brother, he wiped his face with it and behold, the entire handkerchief was soaked with blood. Sorely grieved, he said to himself, 'What can the matter be? After all, my brother took the good road to the right which was to make him a tsar. How is it that he has met his death?' He bade farewell to his wife and father-in-law and rode forth on his heroic horse to locate his brother. After he had travelled a short or a long distance, for a long or a short time, he turned up at that same kingdom where his brother had lived. He made full enquiries and discovered that the prince had indeed gone hunting and disappeared into thin air – not a trace of him could be found anywhere.

Like his brother, Ivan the hero set out on a hunt in the same forest where he also startled the swift-footed stag and was determined to capture it dead or alive. Riding fast in hot pursuit, Ivan came to the same wide meadow where the stag vanished from before his eyes. There, too, was the little stream flowing in the meadow and two grey ducks were swimming on the water. Ivan the soldier's son killed the ducks, came to the white stone palace, and searched the chambers. They were all completely empty except for one room in which there was a lit stove with a large pan standing on the hearth. He roasted the ducks to a turn, took them out into the courtyard, sat on the steps, carved and ate them. Suddenly out of nowhere a beautiful damsel appeared before him and said to him, 'Bread and salt to the welcome guest. But my good youth Ivan, why are you dining in the courtyard?'

'I do not enjoy eating inside,' answered the soldier's son. 'It is much more pleasant out here. Sit down with me and join me in my meal.'

'I would gladly do this, but I fear your enchanted horse,' she replied.

'Have nothing to fear, my lovely damsel. This is an ordinary horse; I have left my magic one at home.' She believed him, and began to swell up and swell up as before, turning into a vicious lioness. Just as she was about to swallow the hero, his magic steed dashed into the courtyard and seized her round the body with his powerful legs. Ivan the soldier's son then produced his sharp sword and cried out in a piercing voice, 'Stand fast, accursed one!

Have you not swallowed whole my brother, Prince Ivan? Disgorge him now, or I shall slice you into a thousand small pieces.'

The lioness spat out Prince Ivan; he was long dead and his body had begun to rot; even the flesh on his face had dried up and fallen off. Ivan the hero took the two phials containing the water of death and the water of life from his saddle. He sprinkled his brother with the water of death, and the flesh grew together. Then he sprinkled him with the water of life and the prince got up and spoke, 'Ah, how long have I been sleeping?'

'You would have slept forever if it were not for me,' answered the hero.

Turning now to the vicious lioness, he drew out his mighty sword and prepared to hew off the vicious beast's head, but she turned back again into a most beautiful maiden of indescribable loveliness, and began in tears to beg and pray for clemency. 'Spare me, good youth, and take pity on me.' Gazing at her exceeding beauty, Ivan the champion had mercy and released her.

Together the brothers went to the palace, held a three-day's feast, and parted from each other. Prince Ivan remained in his kingdom with the thrice-beautiful Princess Nastasia, and Ivan the hero returned to join his wife and father-in-law.

Years passed. One day, Ivan the hero took a walk in the open field. There he came across a young girl who was begging for alms. The soldier's son was strangely moved, drew out a gold coin from his pocket, and handed it to the child. Once the girl took the coin she began to swell up, turned into a savage lioness, and tore the hero in a thousand small pieces. Not long after, the same thing happened to Prince Ivan. He took a walk in his garden and met an old woman who bowed low to him and begged him for alms. The prince handed her a gold coin. Once the woman took the coin she began to swell up, turned into a savage lioness, seized Prince Ivan, and tore him into a thousand small pieces. This was the tragic end of the two Ivans – the sons of the soldier and both mighty heroes – at the hands of the serpents' sister.

3

Legends

Prince Vladimir and the Fall of the Old Gods

Many years before his conversion to the Christian faith, Prince Vladimir, son of Svyatoslav and grandson of Olga the Serene, cruelly murdered his brother Yaropolk, the heir, in order to seize the throne of Kiev. He then began to reign alone and built a magnificent palace of marble and stone at the highest point of the city, above the banks of the Dniepr River.

Vladimir's beautiful wife, Anna, a Christian princess of Byzantium, prayed night and day that he repent of his crime against his brother and turn to the true faith. But many years were to pass before her prayers would be answered, and Vladimir would immerse his naked body in the waters of the Dniepr to accept the faith of Christ.

In the meantime, Vladimir erected statues of the ancient gods on the hill outside the palace courtyard: a wooden Perun with a head of silver and whiskers of gold, Khors, Dazhbog, Stribog, Simargl and Mokosh. The foolish Kievans sacrificed to them, calling them gods. They even brought their sons and daughters and sacrificed them to these demonic idols. Mother Earth was desecrated with their offerings, and the land and the hill of Rus were defiled with the blood of young men and maidens.

In northern Novgorod, Vladimir appointed his uncle Dobrynya to rule and unite the citizens. He, too, set up an idol of the god Perun beside the Volkhov River and the beguiled people of Novgorod offered sacrifices to it as if it were a living god. Perpetual fires of burning oak tended by slaves surrounded the statue of Perun in Novgorod and death was the penalty for anyone who might carelessly allow the flame to be extinguished.

Wishing to thank the gods for victorious expeditions made against the fearsome Pecheneg tribes, Vladimir's military counsellors and chief warriors cast lots among the young men and damsels of Kiev to find a suitable sacrificial victim. On one occasion, the lot fell on the son of a Christian elder who refused to let Vladimir's men lay their hands on the youth, saying, 'Your gods are nothing but wooden idols made by human hands. They can neither eat nor drink nor engage in discourse. Tell your prince this: "There is but one God, the almighty Father who made heaven and earth."'

At this the Kievan warriors advanced and were about to destroy the Christian's property, but he only laughed and mocked them. 'Let us see if one of your gods will himself come and take my son,' he scoffed, 'for I will not surrender him.' Infuriated, the pagans demolished his house and slaughtered the man and his boy together. Both of them immediately joined the ranks of the martyrs in heaven.

Finally, when Prince Vladimir received Christian baptism and repented for his past sins, he directed that all the idols in Kiev be overthrown, smashed, hewn to pieces, or thrown into the fire. The statue of Perun, however, was bound to a horse's tail and dragged down to the river where twelve men were ordered to beat it with rods; not because the wooden god was thought to be sensitive to any pain, but because the evil demon that for so long had deceived the Russians in this guise had to be humiliated and disgraced. As the idol was lugged to the Dniepr, the citizens lamented, for they had not yet been baptized.

Perun was flung into the river, and Vladimir issued the following command: 'If the statue stops, push it out from the banks until it has gone through the rapids; then touch it no more.' This command was duly obeyed, and no sooner had the idol passed through the rapids than it was cast upon the sands. Since that time, this place has been known as Perun's Shore. Where the image once stood, Vladimir constructed a church in honour of Saint Basil the Great.

In Novgorod the old gods were destroyed by Dobrynya, who also commanded that Perun's statue be removed from its place and thrown into the Volkhov River. Beforehand, it was bound with ropes and dragged through the mire to the banks of the river, causing the demon to cry out in anguish. To everyone's astonishment Perun floated against the current and as he passed under a bridge a voice was heard exclaiming, 'This is for you, O citizens of Novgorod, in memory of me.' Even now, it is said, from time to time, on certain days of the year, the voice of Perun may be heard.

The following morning a man named Pyotr, who dwelt on the banks of a small tributary of the Volkhov called the Pidba, spotted the idol floating towards the shore. He quickly grabbed a long pole and thrust the idol away, saying, 'Now, my young Perun, you have had enough to eat and drink; be off with you.'

This brought to an end in a tangible sense the old religion of the Slavs. But although the pagan gods had been annihilated physically, their memory and their deeds lived on in the new faith through legends, epic tales and folklore.

Prince Vladimir's Quest

Great Prince Vladimir, mighty son of Svyatoslav the Good and grandson of Olga the Serene, had united the tribes of ancient Rus – the Polyanians who spoke to the moon; the Derevlians who dreamt dreams of magic mountains, and the Severians who walked through flames. Then he spoke thus to his three most faithful subjects: 'Mine is now a land of plenty, a land of beauty and a land of peace. Only one thing is lacking and without it our new nation can never survive. Neither will it progress to greater wisdom; nor will it comprehend the meaning of life and death.

'That thing is a faith: a faith of truth; a faith of beauty; a faith that will move the hearts of the people of Rus. This faith that I seek has a language that is understood beyond the moon. It believes not in dreams but in visions. Its message, springing from a burning furnace of love, can send the mountains skipping.

'Go, valiant and trustworthy Oleg. Go, Mladan the honourable. Go, brave Vachtan thrice blessed. Set forth to the far corners of the earth and find me this faith which surely dwells in a favoured land beyond our shores. Be pilgrims; be strangers in strange places; respect all people and search diligently for the pearl that will give us life. You will recognize it upon first encounter, upon first sight, at first touch: your hearts will stir with conviction. Pay homage and return to me immediately with the fruits of your mission.'

'Munificent Prince! August Ruler of the lands of Rus! May the years of your life be long and prosperous,' cried the men. 'You, O Vladimir, have created a powerful commonwealth. No longer are we warring tribes or strangers to peace. Under you we have scaled the ladder of civilization and have distanced ourselves from greed and hatred. We were wanderers, now are we settled into communities. We read the stars in vain and in vain did we search for a message.

You have set our sights on the Lord of Truth, the Creator of the Universe and the Architect of Life.

'Your command, O son of Good Svyatoslav, fills our hearts with dread and our minds with doubt. For how can one know the unknowable or approach the unapproachable? How can one divine divinity or impinge on sanctity? What is truth? Will not the ignorance of our pagan past cast a mist over our eyes? Will not the dark and deep shadows of the only beliefs we know prevent us from discerning the light?

'But let us not begin our sacred task with questions and worldly fears. Let us rather set out with the sure belief that the Master Whom we seek will have mercy upon us, guide our footsteps and lead us to his Holy ones. Let us pray that this Lord will bring us to His Holy Wisdom so that our goal, His Kingdom, sets its imprint on our journey.'

From east to west and from north to south, the three envoys carried out the sacred command. Like nomads they wandered over the face of the earth: they thirsted across deserts; they hungered in the wilderness; over the mountain, through valleys, beyond the rivers and lakes, tireless in their search for the Way of Truth.

They visited peoples of all colours, races and creeds, asking the same question of each: 'We are men of Rus, land of the sand-swept steppes, and we seek the religion of truth to strengthen and to save our new nation. What are your beliefs? How do you worship?'

They met the men of the north, tillers of the earth, venerating the spirits of the ground. And those of the south, who fished in the seas, and paid homage to the spirits of the waters. The eastern hunters adored the spirits of the forest while the western philosophers held strange discourse with the spirits of the air.

'Ours is the true religion,' they all declared. 'Come and see our gods in the earth, the rivers, the woods and the sky. Our gods are benevolent providers: grain, fish, meat and water are ours for the taking. We have dominion over the land.'

But Oleg, Mladan and Vachtan did not feel their hearts stir. 'What religions are these,' they thought, 'that ask of men only to receive but never to give; only to exploit but never to create? Where is their love, their service and their sense of beauty? Where is their holiness? We cannot bring tales of these strange gods to the people of Vladimir our Prince. We must persevere in our search, treading the path in places even beyond the seas.'

The weeks passed and so did the months. Towards late afternoon on a dry autumn day, the travellers met a dark and grotesque dwarf named Nalsa at the crossing of two important paths.

'Who are you?' asked the dwarf. 'Where have you come from, and what is the purpose of your journey?'

The three men told Nalsa of their quest.

'Go west into deep Mesopotamia,' he advised, 'and there you will enter Babylon, the celebrated city of the seven hills, with its high walls and its magnificent marble temples. In them the people fall prostrate before the black statue of the awesome goddess Yram, chanting, praising and offering up clouds of rose-scented incense. But I must warn you,' he added, 'if you should meet a maiden on your way, turn away, resist her charms and do not heed her lies, for she will surely lead you to misery and misfortune.'

The men of Rus sped westwards towards Babylon to learn more of this powerful deity. But just as they were about to enter its gates, a tall, veiled woman crossed their path. All three were struck by her serenity and gentleness, all were moved by her sweetness and humility. Their hearts burned within when she called to them by name.

'Hail Oleg, hail Mladan, hail Vachtan! What brings you to this city of waste and prodigality? Turn back; turn east. Follow the rising sun, the righteous Son, who will shine on you with the light of knowledge and lead you to the truth! For what you seek is not to be found among the joyless pagans in their walled sanctuaries of clay. Proceed instead to the Queen of cities that gazes both east and west, where cupolas of gold glisten under brilliant skies and where the sign of the Cross is seen in the clouds. There men know the meaning of love, mercy and hope!'

But the three adventurers remembered the dwarf's warning, so they ignored the promptings of their hearts. Shunning the lady, they marched straight into Babylon and entered the temple. It was the hour of prayer. Aged men in solemn, dark ritual made their bows before Yram's fantastic images of stone and metal. Women in black circled around an incense burner that gave out dense, dark smoke. And all the while the priests and choristers engaged in a hideous discordant chant.

'Let us leave this place,' urged Oleg, 'for the dwarf Nalsa has deceived us. He has led us to a religion that delights in despair, to a goddess who is the embodiment of hopelessness and remorse. Yram is the opponent of life, the courtier of death, the handmaid of evil.'

'You speak our minds,' said Mladan. 'Let us seek out the lady whose words of greeting stirred our souls. She will direct us to that city of promise where there is a living faith and a merciful God.'

Appalled by the stench, noise and misery of Babylon, Vachtan hastened to the city gates to find the gracious lady. But she was nowhere to be seen. Anxiously he asked the sellers of wares, the cobblers and the smiths at the walls, but none could remember seeing her.

Utterly despondent, the three men lifted their eyes to the hills.

'O Great Lord whose name we have yet to learn!' they implored. 'Have mercy and grant us guidance!'

Immediately the words of the lady rang in their ears: 'Turn to the rising sun,' she had said, 'to the city that gazes both east and west. There you will find the religion of truth and beauty, a faith that speaks of life.'

These were words of authority and hope and as one man the three travellers set off. For forty days and nights they journeyed eastward until they reached a wide stretch of water. Unable to proceed and overcome with exhaustion and hunger, the men collapsed under a damp oak tree and fell into a deep sleep. And while they slept, the veiled lady appeared to each of them in a dream.

'Go the nearest village,' she said, 'to the first house on the right. There you will be given food. Wait there, and a sea captain named Kolya will take you in a wooden boat to the place you seek.'

The next morning, Oleg, Mladan and Vachtan were astonished to discover that they had shared the very same dream and immediately they set off for the house, full of expectation and wonder. Each one sensed that the end of their mission was at hand and that all they had endured up to now had served to prepare them for the fulfilment of their hopes.

At the humble house of Raab and Rasa the three visitors were warmly welcomed. In the courtyard, under a shady oak, a table was laid before them. Bread, fish, wine, olives and figs were served to satisfy the men's hunger and to restore their strength. By noon, the sea captain Kolya appeared, just as the lady had predicted. So the guests gave grateful thanks to Raab and Rasa for their hospitality and boarded the sturdy boat *Kivot*.

After a day and a night's sailing, the *Kivot* entered a spacious expanse of iridescent sea that gleamed in the rays of the morning sun. Dolphins danced and bounded in watery arcs around the boat's prow, sending up sprays of salty sea water that sparkled in the shafts of light that arrowed through the sails.

At last they rounded a pine-clad promontory and came upon a glorious sight. A noble city of golden cupolas, white marble and stone palaces rose before them, garlanding the sea which reflected its brilliance. This was the city founded by Constantine the Great, first Emperor of Byzantium, many centuries before: a Christian city whose roads girdled red brick churches, ample squares and grand houses that spilled and tumbled in kaleidoscopic confusion down to the sandy beaches. No matter where one looked the buildings were crowned with a wreath of golden crosses.

'Look!' breathed Vachtan. 'The sign of the cross in the clouds, just as the lady told us! See how it rules the life of the city!'

Twilight fell and the boat pulled into a deep, wide cove. Ahead of them rose a magnificent edifice, of a size they had never before seen or even imagined possible – the cathedral of Holy Wisdom.

The enormous golden dome towered over the city, crowning the cathedral like the vault of Heaven.

In the morning the pilgrims disembarked in haste to absorb more of this astonishing vision. They sped along the road leading to the turreted walls, which were guarded by monumental statues of a Lion, an Eagle, an Ox and a Man, each with penetrating eyes of lapis lazuli glaring down on the three men in solemn indifference. Finally they reached the massive bronze doors of the cathedral and entered reverently and quietly.

At that moment the morning liturgy began. One hundred and fifty priests, deacons, readers, chanters and servers streamed into the nave in three lines from the eastern end of the building. In the centre stood imperial and ecclesiastical dignitaries dressed in jewel-encrusted purple, blue and gold brocade. Crowding around them, the city's faithful bowed and prayed, following the sequence of the sacred ceremony that unfolded before them like an ancient drama.

The men of Rus gazed high at the gilded dome's mosaic above them. Christ the King, the Almighty, turned his divine gaze upon them and tenderly blessed their arrival with his raised right hand. Around him were ranged forty arched windows, through which the rays of the sun fell on the silver chancel rails and the precious, embossed ornaments, and were reflected in a shimmering display of multi-coloured particles that played over the golden mosaics.

A torrent of music resounded in the vast space. Singers in black cassocks filled the air with a psalmody whose harmony and melody defied human description. The three men from the land of Rus were totally overwhelmed.

'Is this not the same music that one hears only in the choirs of the firmament?' they whispered to each other. 'Surely it is not by chance that we have come to this holy place, where men glorify their Master in truth and honour.'

When the travellers returned to their homeland, Prince Vladimir greeted them with respect. 'Nine months to the day have passed, O faithful subjects,' he cried. 'What good word do you bring for the spiritual life of our land?'

'O great Prince,' replied Oleg, 'we beseech you to consider our advice carefully. For we have journeyed far afield and have studied the religions of many peoples. The tillers, the fishers, the hunters and the seers all honour false gods that thrive on pride, idleness, dishonour, greed and arrogance. Powerful Yram of Babylon breeds self-satisfaction and hysteria. She has ensnared her people in prodigality. We had nowhere to go, no one to turn to. In our despondency we raised our eyes heavenward and prayed to the unknown Lord Whom we sought, to lead us along the path of Truth.

'Eventually, a beautiful and queenly lady came to our aid, and with her help we were brought to the Queen of cities, Constantinople, where we witnessed the religion of the Christians. In the Church of Holy Wisdom we saw a beauty that can never be forgotten and a ceremony that glorified Christ, the loving God-man. Language is powerless to express what our eyes have seen, but each of us felt that he had returned to an ancient homeland after a long and fruitless absence. For there we rediscovered our true selves, among people who worshipped in beauty and understood the meaning of joy. Surely God resides with them.'

The great Prince Vladimir wept.

'Your message fills my heart with compunction and a deep gratitude,' he said, 'and I have a burning desire to see these things for myself. I, too, must journey to the land of the Christians. For if this is the foretaste of their faith, if the entrance of the temple is so grand and magnificent, if the splendour of its beauty dazzles the eyes of the soul, then what truth and glory will be found in the innermost shrine? What blessings must there be for the servant of the Saviour? Let all the people of the lands of Rus become followers of Christ, not only for their own lives and their own good, but for the life of the world.'

The Tale of Boris and Gleb

The Russian people honour Boris and Gleb as martyrs – but as martyrs of an unusual sort, unique to Russian piety. For these brothers were not killed to test their Christian faith, but because of an act of non-resistance to the physical power of evil. They chose to die as innocent and voluntary victims in imitation of Christ's sacrificial death. This unusual view of passion-bearing martyrdom identifies a veneration of holy agony and pity for innocent suffering, which the Russian people have displayed at different moments of their history. The cult of Boris and Gleb, their earliest canonized saints, articulates the belief that, ultimately, all innocent and voluntary suffering in the world is suffering which imitates that of Christ in Gethsemane.

Valiant Prince Vladimir, son of Svyatoslav, grandson of Olga, ruled in glory over the Russian land, whose sacred earth he had baptized into the new faith. He protected Rus from the forces of evil arrayed against it, bringing peace and harmony to his subjects. But now, towards the end of his life, the wild Pecheneg nomads began fresh attacks on the Kievan kingdom. To his great sorrow, Vladimir was too ill to lead the battle against them.

Now Vladimir had twelve sons. The eldest was named Svyatopolk, and the next was Yaroslav, but Vladimir's favourites during the last years of his reign were the two youngest, Boris and Gleb.

Svyatopolk, by nature envious and impetuous, had long been jealous of his brothers Boris and Gleb. When his father grew old he planned to have his brothers assassinated, so as to claim the throne for himself. Vladimir came to know of this, however, and sent Svyatopolk into exile. As a result, Svyatopolk conceived a violent hatred for Boris and Gleb.

When the Pechenegs attacked, Vladimir reluctantly called for Boris, his obedient son, to carry out the campaign on his behalf.

'I am ready, my father, to fulfil your wish!' declared Boris. He bowed and kissed the prince's feet to show his fidelity, and embraced him with tears. For it is written that 'A son is obedient to his father and loves him to his mother's face.' And again, 'The clan of the just is blessed, and their family will be blessed.'

Boris conducted a successful campaign, and within two months he had routed the Pechenegs and sent them back across the mountains to their own lands. But just as he was flushed with joy at his victory, a messenger reached him with dreadful news from Kiev. Valiant Prince Vladimir was dead, and with his dying breath had expressed the wish that Boris should succeed him. But Svyatopolk had had Vladimir's body wrapped in a rug and conveyed away secretly at night for burial, and then had promptly seized the throne.

Boris grieved for his father. 'How I wish I could have arranged his burial myself. How I wish I had been there to say farewell to him! But I pray to the Lord to admit Vladimir into the ranks of the righteous in heaven. My father was the light of my eyes; he was dawn's radiance on my face! O Lord our God, in the name of our departed ancestors, receive him with mercy!'

Then Boris turned his thoughts to Svyatopolk. 'He has illegally forced his way onto the throne, and he has irreverently handled the sacred corpse of our father. Now, I know, he wishes to do away with me. I believe my brother is obsessed with worldly cares and thinks of killing me. But I refuse to raise my hand against Svyatopolk, for he is older than I. Now that my father has passed away, let him take the place of my father in my heart.'

And so Boris went towards Kiev as innocently as a lamb and with no evil designs on his brother.

Meanwhile the lawless Svyatopolk planned the cruellest of deeds. He had been told of his brother's absolute loyalty by an informer, but he chose his most vicious follower, Putsha, and ordered him to murder Boris in his tent as he slept. It was not long before Boris received warning of his brother's plot.

'No,' he cried, 'I cannot believe my brother would be so wicked, when he knows I will not fight against him! God be praised. I shall not move from this spot. Neither shall I flee nor resist my elder brother. God's will be done.'

The solders and retainers who had been with Boris in the campaign against the Pechenegs then came to Boris.

'Lay siege to Kiev,' they urged him. 'Drive out Svyatopolk! You are the one chosen to rule over our land.'

'No,' said Boris. 'I shall send messages to my brother asking for clemency, and urging him to disband his army.'

But before long he learnt that some of his brother's men had been seen a few hours' ride away from his own camp. Now at last he believed that his brother wished him ill, and fear entered his heart.

'Lord Jesus Christ,' he prayed, 'let me not perish, but stretch forth thine all-powerful hand to me, a miserable sinner; deliver me from the fury of those who rise up against me; save me in this hour, thou who alone art the refuge of the afflicted.'

But still he would not lift his hand against Svyatopolk. As he had obeyed his father of old, so was he prepared to obey his older brother, even if that meant obedience to death. Boris understood that submission without struggle is the will of God: 'If he sheds my blood and attempts to slay me, then a martyr shall I be unto my Lord. For I shall not resist, because it is written: "God resists the proud, but gives grace to the humble" and "He who says, 'I love God,' and hates his brother, is a liar." And again, "There is no fear in love; perfect love casts out fear." Therefore what shall I say or what shall I do? Behold, I must go to my brother and say, "Be a father to me. You are my brother and elder. What is your command, my lord?"'

As he thought about his impending martyrdom, Boris meditated upon the sufferings and passions of the holy martyrs: Nicetas the Goth, who was brutally tortured and burnt by his own kinsmen; Vaclav the Czech prince, who was murdered by his elder brother; and Barbara, the Roman virgin who died by the hand of her own father.

These thoughts were a comfort to Boris. 'Voluntary suffering is the imitation of Christ, the perfect fulfilment of the Gospel,' he meditated. 'But the glory of this world, rich food and swift horses, great possessions and honours innumerable – all these pass away and are thinner than a cobweb. Had not my ancestors all these things? Yet for them, already, all these things are now as if they never existed. Even Solomon himself, having passed through all and acquired everything, says, "Vanity of vanities: all is vanity."'

As night came he ordered his tent to be erected, withdrew to it, and wept bitterly. But as the hired assassins arrived and approached the tent, what they heard was not weeping, but the pious Boris singing the Vigil Service.

'O Lord, how are they increased who come against me. Many are they that rise up against me.' And later: 'Your arrows have pierced me, for I am ready for wounds, and my pain is before me continually.' And Boris also prayed: 'Lord, hear my prayer, and enter not into judgement with your servant, for no living man shall be just before you. For the enemy has crushed my soul.'

Svyatopolk's men listened in awe. They did not dare interrupt the service, but waited outside the tent until it was finished. At daybreak Matins came to an end. Boris embraced his friends, lay down on his couch and invited those outside to come in and carry out their orders. Boris had the troops to fight back, but he willingly sacrificed his will to God's. What a contrast to the clan-hating Svyatopolk!

'Brethren, approach, complete your work; and peace be with my brother, and with you, brethren. I commend my soul to the Lord, and I submit to God's will. Vouchsafe to accept the passion!' he cried, and tearfully he prepared for his bitter death. 'I thank you, God, for allowing me to suffer everything for the love of your Word. You know, my Lord, that I do not resist, I do not object.'

At last the murderers broke in, fell upon him like wild beasts and plunged their spears into his body.

Boris's beloved Hungarian retainer Georgiy threw himself on top of Boris's body in a sacrificial act of protection but he was soon overpowered and hacked to pieces. Svyatopolk's men saw that Georgiy wore a large gold chain around his neck, which the prince had given him. Rather than waste time taking the chain from the retainer's neck, they cut off his head and grabbed it that way.

Mortally wounded, Boris dragged himself painfully out of his tent and prayed:

O Lord God, I thank you, unworthy though I am,
for allowing me to partake of the passion of your Son,
our Lord Jesus Christ.
For you have sent your only-begotten Son into the World,
and evil men put him to death.
I, too, was sent by my father
to save our people from the pagans who rose up against him,
and now I am attacked by my brother's men.

Lord, forgive them their sins.
Grant that I may rest with the saints;
do not deliver me into the hands of the enemy.
You, O Lord, are my defence
and into your hands I commend my spirit.

Eventually, one of the assassins returned, and plunged a sword into Boris's heart. Then the body was wrapped in canvas, loaded upon a waggon and taken to Vyshegorod. There it was buried in the church of Saint Basil the Great.

Svyatopolk now turned his attention to his youngest brother.

'Behold, I have killed Boris; now how can I kill Gleb?'

Once more he adopted the devices of Cain. He sent messages to Gleb: 'Come quickly, our father is very ill and desires your presence!'

Gleb was always obedient to his father, so he quickly mounted his horse, and set out with a small company. He had journeyed as far as Smolensk, when he received a message of warning from Yaroslav, his older brother, who told him of their father's death and of the brutal killing of Boris. When he heard this news, Gleb burst into tears and lamented for his father, but still more deeply for his brother.

'Why did this have to come about, and not even from an enemy but from our own princely brother?'

But he too would take no action to save himself from the impending treachery.

Woe is me, O Lord.
It were better for me to die with my brother
than to live on in this world.
O Boris, had I but seen your angelic countenance,
I should have died with you.
Why am I now left alone?
Where are your words that you once spoke to me, O brother?
No longer do I hear your sweet counsel.
If you have received affliction from God,
pray for me that I may endure the same passion.
For it were better for me to dwell with you
than in this deceitful world.

From Smolensk, Gleb set out by boat for the capital. But Svyatopolk's sailors had orders to put him to death at once, and they intercepted him. When Gleb saw them approaching, he ordered his followers to offer no resistance.

'Leave me behind,' he told them, and thought to himself, 'Perhaps they will capture me alone and take me before my brother. Then, surely, he will show me mercy. Even if I fail in this, I alone shall die, and the others will go safely.'

But as he saw the enemy boats approaching, the prince grew fearful and implored: 'Plead my cause, O Lord, and fight against them that do me harm. Lay your hand upon the shield and buckler, and stand up to help me.'

As his murderers confronted him, he protested his innocence, and pleaded for mercy: 'Have mercy on my youth, have mercy, my lords! You shall be my masters, and I your slave. Do not tear me from my life that has not yet ripened, do not reap the unripe ear of corn. Do not cut down the vine that has not yet grown up.'

Gleb begged to be taken to Svyatopolk but the men refused.

'Vladimir, Vladimir, my father and lord,' wept Gleb, 'incline your ear and hear my voice. Look down and see what is happening to your young child, how I am being slaughtered in my innocence!

'Hearken, O heaven, and attend, O earth!

'And you, my brother Boris, hear my voice! For though I summoned my father, Vladimir, he made no response. Do you, too, wish to abandon me? See the grief in my heart and the wound in my soul! See my tears flowing like a river! Yet no one heeds me. But you, O Boris, remember me. Pray to our Lord on my behalf, for you stand by His throne and possess great courage.'

Then, bending his knees, Gleb began to pray to God: 'Most compassionate and most merciful Lord! Do not turn from my tears, but have pity on my grievous helplessness. Look down on the crushing of my heart. For I am being slaughtered and know not why, nor understand for what wrong. But it is written that the innocent shall be betrayed by parents and brethren, and kinsfolk and friends; and a brother will cause his kinsman to be put to death.

'Bestow on me the strength and courage, O Saviour, to endure the same trials as my brother so that together we may live for ever in your holy kingdom.'

The villains leaped into Gleb's boat. In their hands were naked swords, which glittered like the water. Svyatopolk's cursed messenger, Goriaser, ordered Torchin, Gleb's cook, to draw his knife and kill his master. Unlike the blessed Georgiy who shielded the body of his master, Prince Boris, Torchin turned on Gleb and slaughtered him.

Just as Abel was killed by his jealous brother, Gleb was offered up as a sacrifice to God like a guileless lamb, a glorious offering amid the perfume of incense. In heaven he received the martyr's crown of glory with his brother. Their bodies were together, and far more were their souls, dwelling with the Master and King of all, in infinite joy, in ineffable light. Now, from heaven, they bestow miraculous gifts upon the holy land of Russia, which they protect as saintly princes. They grant healing to those who draw near with faith, making the lame to walk, the blind to see, the sick healthy, the captives free, and giving relief to the oppressed.

Gleb's body was thrown upon the river bank to rot between two tree trunks, and the murderers returned to Kiev to give an account of their mission to Svyatopolk. 'We have done as you commanded,' they said; and Svyatopolk exalted in his heart.

But Yaroslav, enraged by these acts of fratricide, pursued his evil brother and fought many battles against him. At length the two armies were face to face at the Alta river. Yaroslav lifted up his hands to heaven and cried, 'Behold, the blood of my brothers cries out to you, O Lord, just as the blood of Abel did in times past. Avenge these just martyrs too. Visit upon Svyatopolk the sorrow and terror that you inflicted on Cain to avenge the blood of Abel.'

When he had finished praying, the two armies advanced against one another, and the plain of the Alta was covered with a multitude of soldiers. It was then Friday. As the sun rose, they met in battle. The carnage was terrible, such as had never before occurred in Rus. The soldiers fought hand to hand and slaughtered each other. Three times they clashed, and battled through the entire day, so that the blood flowed in the valley. Towards evening, Yaroslav's army triumphed and the accursed Svyatopolk fled.

As he fled, a demon fell upon him and his bones became weak, so that he was unable even to sit on his horse. They had to carry him on a litter. Pursued by the wrath of God he was borne first to Brest, then to the land of the Lyakhs and finally into the wilderness between Poland and Bohemia where he was dealt a fatal wound and forfeited his life. At last he received his just reward from the Lord, for since his death he abides in bonds and eternal torment. His tomb stands in the wilderness, even to this day, and from it issues forth an evil stench as a lesson to humankind.

When Yaroslav eventually occupied the throne of Kiev, he ordered a search to be made for Gleb's corpse. But it could not be found. Some years later, however, huntsmen came upon an intact body, completely untouched by wild beasts. When they heard about this, the elders of the nearest town approached to examine it, and they saw that it shone like a flash of lightning. Certain that this was Gleb's body, they quickly sent word to Yaroslav, who ordered it to be taken to Vyshegorod to be placed beside Boris in the church of Saint Basil, where they both still remain today. How fine and beautiful it is for two brothers to live eternally together.

Shortly after their union in the common grave, miracles began to be seen over their shrine. A soldier inadvertently stepped on the site, and at once a pillar of fire rose up, burning his feet. The singing of angels was heard, and miraculous healings took place through the intercession of the saintly brothers.

The two princes had been taken by stealth but had offered no resistance, despite the advice of those nearest to them. And, like Jesus at Golgotha, they were unjustly put to death by those closest to them in ties of blood and allegiance, yet they forgave their executioners and prayed for them. Finally, like the Lord, they knew the final anguish before death and the temptation to follow their own will instead of God's. But, like Christ, they were able to submit to the will of God even when this meant the sacrifice of their own lives.

4

Epics

Volga the Hero

The blood red sun set behind the dark woods, behind the broad blue sea, behind the lofty mountains. Countless stars appeared in the clear heavens and the bright moon shone; then was Volga Vseslavich the Hero, the son of Marfa and a Dragon, the nephew of valiant Prince Vladimir of Kiev, born in Holy Russia. Moist Mother Earth was his cradle and she rocked and quaked at his nativity. There was a great storm upon the blue sea, the birds flew up to the clouds and the fish swam down into the deeps. The great aurochs and the deer fled over the hills, the hares and rabbits ran into the thick forest, while wolves and bears scattered among the fir trees, and the sables and martens escaped to the islands. For all creation knew that a great hero was born this day in Mother Russia.

When Volga was an hour and a half old he spoke with a voice like thunder, and said, 'Come, my mother Marfa. Dress me not in swaddling clothes, neither gird me about with sashes of silk. But swathe me, Mother mine, in strong steel mail. On my head place a helmet of gold; in my right hand a heavy mace of lead, three hundred pounds in weight.'

By the time Volga was seven years old his mother had taught him to read, and she made him write with a pen. In due course he learned all the wisdom and all the cunning of the birds, the fish and the beasts. He even understood their speech and conversed with them. At ten years of age much magic was revealed to him. At one moment he could turn himself into a bright falcon, at the next into a grey wolf, and then into a brown aurochs with hoofs of gold.

When Volga was fifteen he called together his friends and comrades, and formed a bodyguard of thirty heroes save one; he himself was the thirtieth. He became their leader and took them with him on his journeys across the rugged steppes. Moreover, he provided for them all and gave them an abundance of food and drink, and many sugar delicacies. He also gave them warm clothes; fur coats made of the skins of the marten, the sable and the panther. When his comrades slept, Volga stayed awake. Sometimes he turned himself into a grey wolf and ran and leapt in the dark forest, killing moose-deer, bears and wolves. Martens and panthers were his favourite prey, and he spared neither hares nor foxes. At other times he turned himself into a bright falcon and flew far away over the blue sea, hunting geese and white swans, and not sparing the little grey ducks.

One day when he was in Kiev, he called to his fellows: 'My bold and good comrades, listen to and obey your elder brother and chief! Weave snares of silken cords, spread them on the moist earth in the forest, and catch martens, foxes, black sables and other wild beasts, hunting these for the period of three days and three nights.'

His good companions heard their elder brother and chief, and did the thing commanded. They spread silken cords across the dark forest, over the moist earth – but not a single creature could they take. Then Volga the Hero transformed himself into a growling lion and leapt and bounded over the moist earth, through the gloomy forest, driving out martens, foxes, black sables and other wild beasts, big-bounding hares and little ermines, capturing as many as he could.

Yet again, on a day when Volga was in Kiev with his twenty-nine heroes, he said to them: 'My bold and good comrades, listen to and obey your elder brother and chief! Twine now mighty silken snares. Fasten them to the topmost crests of the trees in the dark forest; and in them catch geese, swans, bright falcons and little singing birds. Do this for the period of three days and three nights.'

The men heard their elder brother and chief, and did the thing commanded. They took snares of silk and set them in the dark forest at the topmost crests of the trees: but not a single creature could they take. Then Volga the Hero transformed himself into an eagle and flew up to the clouds, striking down geese, swans, bright falcons and little singing birds, capturing as many as he could.

Yet again, on a day when Volga was in Kiev with his twenty-nine heroes, he said to them: 'My bold and good comrades, listen to and obey your elder brother and chief! Take sharp axes of stout metal, good for cutting wood, and build oaken vessels. Weave fishing nets of silk and go forth upon the blue sea to catch salmon, dolphins, pikes, flat fish and precious sturgeons. Continue to fish for three days and as many nights.'

And they hearkened to their elder brother and chief, and did the thing commanded. They took sharp axes of stout metal, good for cutting wood, and built oaken vessels. They wove fishing nets of silk and went forth upon the blue sea to fish, but not a single fish could they catch. Then Volga the Hero transformed himself into an enormous pike and plunged into the depths of the blue sea, sending up salmon, dolphins, pikes, flat fish and precious sturgeons, capturing as many as he could.

Yet again, when Volga was in Kiev with his twenty-nine heroes, he said to them, 'My bold and good comrades, listen to and obey your elder brother and chief! Who shall we send to the land of the Tatars, to learn the khan's mind – what plans he is planning – whether or not he intends to invade Holy Russia? If we send an old man he will go slowly, and we shall have long to wait. If we send a middle-aged man he will tarry and drink by the way. If we send a young man he will sport with the maidens, make merry with the wives and chatter with the old crones, in which case we shall have long to wait. It is plain that Volga must go himself.'

Then Volga the leader turned himself into a little bird and flew above Mother Earth. On through the sky he flew and soon came to the land of the Tatars, ruled by Khan Santal. Volga came to the house of the khan and lighted at his little window where he overheard the secret talk between Santal and his wife.

'Ah, my gracious Pantalovna. I know what I know. In Russia the grass does not grow as of old; the flowers do not bloom as of old. It is clear that Volga is no longer alive. So I shall invade Holy Russia and take for myself nine towns, one for each of my nine sons. And to you, Pantalovna, I shall present a costly mantle of fur.'

To this Pantalovna replied: 'Ah, my Khan Santal, lord of the Tatars. I know what I know. In Russia the grass grows just as before and the flowers bloom just as before. Last night I slept, and in my sleep I dreamed a dream. I saw a tiny titmouse fly from the east, and from the west came a black raven. They flew together down into the open plain and tore at one another. The tiny bird tore the black raven asunder, plucked out all its feathers, and scattered them to the winds. That was the hero Volga Vseslavich, but the black raven was the Tatar Santal.'

The khan answered her: 'Ah, my gracious Pantalovna, I intend to ride at once into Holy Russia where I shall take nine cities, one for each of my nine sons. But the costly mantle of fur shall I keep for myself.'

Said the gracious Pantalovna: 'You shall never take nine cities from Holy Russia; nor shall you fetch for yourself a costly mantle of fur.'

The Tatar khan answered in a rage: 'You old devil; you have but slept and dreamed an idle dream.' And with that he struck her upon her white face, and, turning, smote the other cheek, and flung Pantalovna upon the floor of brick; and yet a second time he flung her. 'Nay, but I shall go to Holy Russia,' shouted Santal, 'and I shall take nine cities, one for each of my nine sons, and a costly mantle of fur for myself.'

Then Volga the Hero flew down from the window ledge to the ground, took the form of a grey wolf, and jumped into the stable yard. Going from one good steed to another, he tore out the throat of every one. After this Volga turned himself into a little ermine and slipped into the armoury where the khan kept a great stock of weapons for his men. He snapped all the stout bows, tore out the silken bow-strings, destroyed the fiery arrows and bit notches in the sharp swords. Again Volga, as a little bird, flew back to Kiev and in his own youthful form he addressed his comrades: 'My bold and good comrades, listen to and obey your elder brother and chief! Let us go now to the land of the Tatars.' So they rode thither, and took all the enemy host captive.

'My bold and good comrades,' declared the hero leader, 'let us divide the spoil.'

What lot was valued highly, and what was cheap? Good steeds fetched as much as seven roubles, sharp swords fetched six, weapons of damascened steel were rated at five roubles, steel maces at four. But one lot went very cheaply – the women. Old women were valued at a quarter of a kopeck, young women at half a kopeck and beauties at a copper farthing!

Volga and Mikula

This story is part of a series recounting how the followers of Volga were assembled.

Valiant Prince Vladimir of Kiev had bestowed upon his beloved nephew Volga Vseslavich the three cities Kurtzovets, Oryekovets and Krestyanovets, together with their peasants. For Volga had traversed many lands and conquered many barbaric hordes. He had collected gifts in tribute from many rulers and kings, and had brought them to the royal city of Kiev, to his uncle Prince Vladimir. Much gold had been collected, also silver and great pearls, and large quantities of Arabian bronze which neither darkens nor corrodes, and is more precious than gold or pearls or silver.

Now in these three glorious cities given to him by his uncle Vladimir dwelt stubborn and disloyal people who obeyed no man, and gave neither gifts nor tribute to any. So young Volga Vseslavich assembled his comrades and set out through the free and open plain to collect taxes and the yearly tributes. As they rode, Volga heard a ploughman whistling and calling to his horse; he also heard the man's plough scraping over the ground and grating against the stones. But the ploughman, his horse and his plough were out of sight on the boundless plain.

Volga and his companions rode in quest of the ploughman. A whole day they rode until evening, ever hearing the plough grate and scrape through the plain. But no matter how fast they rode, they could never catch up with the ploughman. And Volga continued to ride the whole of another day, from morning until dusk, but he could not overtake the ploughman. It was only on the third day, just before noon, that Volga and his troop came upon the ploughman driving his plough in the open field. Whistling as he ploughed, the man cast aside great stones and clods of earth from each side of the furrow. He ripped up damp oaks, stumps and tree roots, and his light bay mare was named 'Headraiser', for she would lift her head into the clouds.

The man's plough was made of wood, the mare's reins of silk, the ploughshare was of damascened steel with fittings of silver and handles of pure gold. He himself was a wonder to behold: handsome, muscular and of great height. His sable black curls waved over his forehead and his eyes were as sharp as the falcon's. His shoes were of green Morocco leather with pointed toes and high heels; and under the hollow of his foot, sparrows would have been able to fly. His hat was of fur and his caftan of black velvet.

When Volga reached the ploughman, he addressed him with these words, 'God aid you, ploughman, in your ploughing and tilling.'

'Greetings to you, Volga, and to your men. I do indeed need the help of God in my peasant's work. And where might you be going with your troop of brave comrades?'

'Ah, good ploughman, I go to the three cities which valiant Prince Vladimir has given to me in order to claim my tributes and taxes. First to Kurtzovets, then to Oryekovets, and finally to Krestyanovets.'

'Beware, Volga Vseslavich, for outlaws and highwaymen live there. They lie in wait near the bridge over the Smorodina River. For they saw through the bridge's wooden planks in order that innocent passers-by will fall into the water and drown. Beware, for the same may happen to you. Why, only two days ago I was over in that region with my bay mare and carried away with me two sacks of salt, just two sacks of salt (each of fourteen hundred pounds weight) and the thieving peasants demanded toll. No matter how much I gave them, they asked for more. But I had my whip for the journey, and I paid them their toll with my whip. I felled a thousand of them with one sweep. Those who were upright ended seated, those who were seated ended up flat on their backs, and those who were stretched out will never get up again.'

Hearing this, Volga invited the ploughman to join him and his band of heroes, so the man removed his mare from the plough and mounted her for the journey. But very soon he became troubled by a thought. 'Now, Volga,' he cried, 'I have abandoned my plough in the furrow where it may be discovered by any passer-by and stolen. My brother peasants could make good use of it. Would it not be better to pull the plough out of the ground, scrape the soil from its blade, and hide it in the willow bushes?' So Volga despatched five strong young men from his troop to pull the plough out of the ground, scrape the soil from its blade, and hide it in the willow bushes. When they came up to the maplewood plough, they pulled and twisted the handles this way and that, but they could not remove it from the furrow.

Volga then sent thither ten brave men, but they could do nothing either. Finally he sent the entire troop but still they could do nothing. Then the ploughman himself rode upon his mare to this plough of maplewood. With one hand he took hold of it, pulled it out of the ground, shook the earth from its blade, and hid it in the willow bushes. After this they all rode off once more.

Headraiser the mare began to sprint ahead, forcing Volga's steed to gallop hard in order to keep up. Faster and faster went the mare, her tail spread out behind and her mane waving in the breeze. Volga was left far behind, for spur on as he would, he could barely keep the ploughman in sight. Then Volga began to wave his cap in the air and to shout: 'Stop, stop, good ploughman. If this mare of yours were a stallion, five hundred roubles might I give for her.'

'You are very foolish, Volga Vseslavich,' answered the ploughman. 'When I bought this mare as a foal from her mother's side, I paid five hundred roubles for her then. If this mare were a stallion, she would be priceless!'

'Well, then, tell me your name, bold ploughman, and that of your father,' asked Volga.

The man answered in this fashion:

'When I plough the field for rye and stack it in the rick;
When I stack it in the rick and bring it to the home;
When I bring it to the home and thresh the grain;
When I thresh the grain and brew it,
I give kvas to the peasants to drink.
Then the peasants sing my praises
And call me Young Mikula Selyaninovich, the villager's son.'

Svyatogor, Mother Earth and Destiny

Svyatogor was a giant hero of ancient Rus. His name, meaning 'holy mountain', is derived from his place of dwelling in the 'Holy Mountains'. But where these mountains are geographically and what they represent is not entirely clear. In terms of mythology, they could be associated with the clouds.

Svyatogor was the only giant hero who did not wage a war against Mother Russia; in fact, he was forbidden to enter her territories. As the tall cloud-mountain he dies, fettered with cold, and falls into his winter sleep. The descent of the frost is like the clamping of the iron bands upon the frozen, stone-like earth. Svyatogor's enormous battle sword of steel is the lightning which in spring and summer parts the heavens. During the heavy autumnal storms, it prepares the iron bands which the cold hand of winter lays upon the cloud-mountain.

The giant hero Svyatogor was enormous. So tall was he that his head touched the clouds, and so strong that he could even set the whole world in motion. But his size and strength were like a heavy burden that he was destined to support for ever. There was none with whom he could measure the strength that flowed so fiercely through his veins. So large and powerful was he that Moist Mother Earth could not carry him. She forbade him to enter Holy Russia and he was condemned to live on the distant Holy Mountains in total solitude.

Now he sat on the mountain top, furious with anger. He had had enough of his exile.

'Why can I not walk freely on the open steppes of my country?' he asked himself. 'Why must I be left to endure alone the great weight of my own might? My young heart yearns for freedom; the energy in my sinews is set to burst.' And he angrily tossed his steel club high into the cloudy heavens. Up and up it soared, until it vanished from sight, circled the celestial sphere above Russia, and returned to his ready open hand.

Foolishly, he began to boast to Mother Earth and to Father Sky. 'If I should take to walking on the earth, I would fasten a ring to heaven and bind an iron chain to the ring. Then I would drag the great sky down to Mother Earth. I would turn the earth on its end. I would turn her topsy turvy. And I would confound earth with heaven and heaven with earth!' Thus rashly did Svyatogor boast. Defiantly, he saddled his heroic steed and rode forth onto the verdant steppes – onto the soil of Holy Russia that trembled beneath his weight.

As he looked towards the distant horizon, Svyatogor espied a handsome young man walking slowly across the plain, with a two-pouched skin bag slung across his broad shoulders. Svyatogor dug his heels into the flank of his steed and brought the beast to a gallop. He set his aim on the stranger, to overtake him and question him. The good youth was on foot but not even the best efforts of his mighty horse could bring Svyatogor near him. The youth walked ahead. He never hurried, but the foaming horse could not overtake him.

'Ho, there, wayfarer, brave lad!' cried Svyatogor to the boy. 'Wait a moment; just a short moment. You walk; you do not hurry. But I put my good steed to the gallop with all his equine might. How is it that his four feet are no match for your two?' The good and youthful traveller stopped in his tracks and waited for the giant. From his sturdy shoulders he released the twin-pouched bag of skin and laid it on the moist earth.

The giant dismounted and addressed the youth. 'Tell me, good fellow, what kind of load do you have in your bag?'

'Oh, great and mighty hero,' responded the wayfarer, 'try to lift my load. Your arms are strong, your shoulders broad. Lift my load and take it with you along the verdant plain. Raise it from the earth and you will learn soon enough what it is made of.'

A bag so small was scarcely a challenge for Svyatogor. With his staff in his hand he approached it boldly, and struck it with the wood. It did not budge. He touched it with his finger – it did not move. The little shoulder bag did not stir from its place on the moist earth. Then he seized it with one hand, but could not raise it at all. He laid hold of it with both his hands – not a hair's breadth did it move from its place.

In desperation, he clutched at the bag and heaved with all his mighty force. All he succeeded in doing was to drive himself into the damp earth, up to his knees. Crying and groaning, he fell on the bag. He pressed his heroic bosom against it. Not tears, but blood streamed down his rugged face. His noble heart was spent, but still not so much as a breath of wind could pass under that little shoulder bag.

With half his body buried in the armless grip of Moist Mother Earth, Svyatogor groaned, 'I never lifted such a load! I am very strong – but not strong enough for that. What is the burden that you have in that bag? And you, who are you, bold and noble youth? What is your name and that of your father?'

'O proud Svyatogor,' the mysterious youth replied, 'the weight of the whole world is fully contained herein: Mother Earth and Father Sky, whose strength is greater than that of any mortal being. And I myself am Mikula Selyaninovich, the villager's son. You boasted that you would turn the earth on its end. Now you have indeed found the weight of the earth, and the gods have punished you for your pride.'

'Tell me then, Mikula, for clearly you are one who knows, how may one learn the will of the gods?'

'Arise from your earthen bed and continue your journey. Ride on the straight way until you meet a fork in the road. At that parting, take the left path and gallop ahead at full speed until you come at last to the Northern Mountains. In those mountains, beneath a great oak tree, stands a smithy. You must enquire your fate of the smith therein.'

Svyatogor rode for three days as Mikula commanded, and came to the great tree and to the smithy, and there stood the smith forging two fine threads.

'My greetings to you, master smith. What are you forging?'

'I forge the fates of those who will wed,' answered the smith.

'And who shall I wed?'

'Your bride is in the kingdom by the sea, in the royal city. For thirty years she has lain on a dung heap.'

'Can this be so?' thought the giant Svyatogor 'In that case I shall go to that kingdom by the sea and slay my bride.'

So off he went to the royal city of that kingdom by the sea, and he came to a miserable hut, which he entered. He found no one there save a damsel lying on dungheap. Her skin was as rough and cracked as the bark of the fir tree. Svyatogor took out five hundred roubles and laid them on the table. Then he took his sharp blade and smote her on her breast and departed from that kingdom. When he had gone, the damsel woke and gazed about her. The fir bark fell from her limbs and she became a beauty such as was never seen or heard of in all the world.

From the table she took the five hundred roubles and began to trade, buying and selling goods. So successful was her commerce that gradually she accumulated an untold treasure of gold. With this treasure she built dark red ships, loaded with precious wares, that sailed upon the distant blue seas. At last she came to the great city of Kiev, to the Holy Mountains, and began to barter her precious wares. The fame of her beauty spread all through the town and kingdom, and all men come to look upon her and marvel at her fairness. One day, Svyatogor the Hero also came to gaze upon her beauty. He was captivated, fell in love with her, and began to woo her for himself. Before long they were married.

Then one day he noticed a scar upon his wife's white bosom. 'What is this scar?' he asked her.

'In our kingdom by the sea,' answered his wife, 'I lay asleep for thirty years on a dung heap. Fir bark had crusted my body. Then one day an unknown man came to our hut and left five hundred roubles in gold. When I awoke there was a scar on my bosom, and the fir bark had fallen away from my white body.'

Then Svyatogor the hero realized that none may escape the destiny that is written down of old. Nor may anyone flee upon his good steed from the judgement of the gods.

Ilya of Murom and Svyatogor the Hero

In the hamlet of Karacharof, near the town of Murom, there lived long ago a farmer called Ivan, with his wife and family. He and his wife and his sons and daughters worked hard in the fields; all but one son, Ilya, who was always sitting at home. Because of his grandfather's sin, Ilya had neither arms nor legs. For thirty years he sat by the oven, unable to do anything without help.

And when thirty years were passed, one summer, at the time of haying, his mother and father went out to clear the forest-girdled meadows, leaving Ilya alone in the cottage. He was sitting by the oven as usual when three wayfarers passed by. They were too old and too lame to work, but they had made the pilgrimage to the Holy Land and now wandered about the country singing psalms and living upon the food and money that kind folk gave them. They saw Ilya through the window and called out: 'Ilya! Ilya of Murom! Open wide your gate for the pilgrims. Let us into your cottage. Fetch us a beverage to quench your thirst.'

Ilya of Murom answered, 'Alas, good pilgrims, good elders, my friends. I cannot rise to open the gate for I have been sitting here these thirty years. Gladly would I give you to drink but I can use neither hands nor feet.'

Again the wayfarers called to him, 'Ilya, rise upon your nimble feet and wash your face. Open wide the gate and let the pilgrims in to visit you in your cottage.'

Then Ilya stood on his feet and walked as though nothing ailed him. He reached out and opened wide the gate to let the pilgrims into the cottage. Straight away he brought them some kvas which they took and drank, and then offered it to Ilya, saying, 'Now you drink, Ilya, son of Ivan.' When he had drunk, Ilya felt a rush of warmth throughout his body and his heroic heart burned within him.

'How is your strength now?' they asked.

'Venerable elders,' replied Ilya, 'I thank you humbly. There is a very great strength within me, so much so that I could even move the earth. In fact, if there were a pillar from earth to heaven, and if there were a gold ring attached to the pillar, I would take it by the ring and overturn Holy Russia.'

Then the men looked each upon the other, and said: 'Give us to drink yet again.' And Ilya brought more kvas for the pilgrims. When they had drunk, they gave the cup to him a second time. Ilya emptied the cup in one draught, without drawing breath.

'How is it with you now, Ilya?' they inquired.

'The strength I feel is indeed very great,' said Ilya, 'but only half as much as my former strength.'

'Let it be so,' said the wandering pilgrims, 'for if we give you more, Mother Earth will not bear you up. You will be a great hero, O Ilya, and it is not written that you should die in battle. You may fight against all infidel hosts, bold warriors and daring heroes, and defend yourself against them. Only do not go out to fight with the hero Svyatogor, for with his strength he could lift the earth; and fight not with Mikula Selyaninovich, the villager's son, for he is yet stronger and beloved of Moist Mother Earth. Neither contend against Volga, son of Svyatoslav: he will overpower you not by might but by craft and cunning. Against these three have no dispute.

'Do not live at home; do not labour, but go the royal city of Kiev. Now rise up, Ilya, mount your horse and ride out into the free and open plain. Buy the first foal you see with its dam, and after three months you may put a saddle on it. Feed it on millet and maize; walk it about for three months, then keep it for three nights in the garden, and roll the foal three mornings in the dew. Finally, lead it to a high fence, and when it easily leaps the fence both from this side and that, then ride it wherever you wish: it will carry you.'

After these words the men vanished.

Then Ilya went forth to his father in the clearing and found him with his mother, brothers and sisters asleep, tired out from their toil. He took up their axes and began to hew the brushwood from its roots and throw it all onto a pile on the edge of the field. Ilya worked so hard and so fast that what the others might have done in three days, he achieved in the space of one hour. Having thus felled a whole field of timber, he drove the axes deep into a stump from which no man could draw them.

When his parents and family awoke and saw the axes, they marvelled.

'Who has done this?' they said.

Then Ilya came from the forest and drew the axes from the stump; and his father gave thanks to God that his son had become whole and was so famous a workman. 'Come, father, mother, brothers and sisters. Is not your field well cleared for the ploughing? Now I must say farewell to home.'

With his parents' blessing Ilya set off and rode on his good horse into the free and open plain.

On his way, he met a peasant leading a shaggy brown foal, the first he had seen, and its dam. What the peasant demanded for the foal, Ilya paid, and for the space of three months he kept the foal in a stall, feeding it with the finest millet and maize. After those three months had passed, he bound the foal for three nights in the garden, and rolled it three mornings in the dew. When that was done, he led the foal to a lofty fence, and the good steed began to leap from side to side. Only then was it able to sustain Ilya's enormous frame, for it had become a heroic steed. All this Ilya did according to the commandments of the elderly psalm-singers who had healed him. Ilya named this noble horse 'Cloudfall'.

Then Ilya saddled Cloudfall, and rode ever further into the wild open plain, until at last he came to a high mountain. When he reached the mountain he scaled it, and then lay down to rest. For twelve days he slept the sleep of a hero. When he awoke, he saw at a little distance a tent of white linen pitched under a mossy oak; and in the tent was a great bed seventy feet long and forty-two feet wide. So he tethered his good steed Cloudfall to the mossy oak, stretched himself upon that heroic bed and fell asleep. Now a hero's sleep is very deep: three days and nights he slept.

On the third day, good Cloudfall heard a mighty clamour from the north. Moist Mother Earth rocked, the dark forests staggered, the rivers overflowed their steep banks. Then the good steed beat upon the earth with his hoof, but could not wake Ilya of Murom. At last the horse shouted out with a human voice,

'Ho there, Ilya of Murom! You sleep there and take your rest, but little do you know of the ill fortune that hangs over you. The hero Svyatogor approaches his tent. Let me loose that I may flee across the open plain; and you may climb up into the mossy oak.' Then Ilya sprang to his nimble feet. He loosed his horse's bridle, set it free to gallop across the plain, and climbed into the giant mossy oak.

And behold! From there he spied the hero coming on his great horse. Taller than the standing forest was he, and his head rested upon the moving clouds. On his shoulder he bore a large casket of crystal, which, when he reached the oak where Ilya hid, he set upon the ground and opened with a golden key. Out of the casket stepped the hero's wife. In all the fair world, no such beauty had ever been seen or heard of; lofty was she of stature and delicate her walk. She had eyes like the eyes of the bright falcon, eyebrows of the blackest sable, dark hair that swayed in the breeze, and her ivory-white body was beyond compare.

As soon as she came out of the crystal casket she set to work to lay the table for her husband's dinner. Spreading a bright chequered cloth on the table, she took from the casket a bottle of mead, a cup and many sweetmeats, and placed them upon it. So they feasted and made merry. And when Svyatogor had eaten and drunk, he lay down to sleep on his great bed in the tent. But his fair, heroic wife went out to walk upon the open plain.

She soon caught sight of Ilya in the oak. 'Come down now, O good and stately youth,' she cried, 'descend from that mossy oak and speak to me, otherwise I shall awaken the giant Svyatogor and complain to him of your discourtesy toward me.'

Ilya could not contend against the woman, and so slipped down from the oak as she had commanded. When her husband was about to rouse from his heavy sleep she put Ilya in Svyatogor's deep pocket. Then the giant once more placed his wife in the crystal casket, locked it with his golden key, lifted it onto his shoulder, mounted his good steed, and set off towards the Holy Mountains.

After a little, the beast kept stumbling, so the hero began to beat him on his stout flanks with a silken whip. Then the horse said in human speech: 'This morning I was carrying a hero and a hero's wife, but now I am carrying two heroes as well as the hero's wife. Is it any wonder that I stumble?'

A puzzled Svyatogor looked around and saw no one. But then he put his hand into his deep pocket where he found Ilya. Drawing him out, he began to question him: 'Who are you? How did you come to be in my pocket?'

Ilya kept no secrets from him, and told him how Svyatogor's wife had spied him in the oak, called him down, and then put him in his pocket. When he heard it, Svyatogor blazed with anger. He turned on his faithless wife and killed her for trying to deceive him.

The hero Svyatogor was pleased that Ilya had spoken honestly, and there arose a great friendship between them. Svyatogor exchanged crosses with Ilya in token of their friendship, and called Ilya his younger brother. He taught Ilya all the techniques of handling weapons, how to use his mace, bow and arrows and spear in fighting, as well as all the paths and ways known to the famous heroes. And as they talked together, Ilya said, 'How dearly do I wish to see Svyatogor, that great hero; but he no longer rides on Moist Mother Earth, neither does he show himself in Russia amongst our company of heroes.'

'I am he,' said Svyatogor. 'Gladly would I ride among you, but Moist Mother Earth will not bear me up. And what is more, I may no longer ride in the plains of Holy Russia, but only on the lofty hills and steep precipices. Let us now ride among the crags, and come with me to the Holy Mountains.' Ilya called up his good horse from the plain by a loud whistle, and the two heroes, the old Svyatogor and the younger Ilya of Murom, rode on together.

On the way Svyatogor said to Ilya, 'When we come to my dwelling, the palace of white stone, and I lead you to my father, warm a piece of iron, and do not give him your hand.'

So when they came to the Holy Mountains, to the palace of white stone, Svyatogor's aged father cried, 'Ho, my dear child. Have you been far afield?'

'I have been to look on Holy Russia, father.'

'What have you seen and heard there?'

'Nothing have I seen or heard in Holy Russia, but I have brought with me a hero from there.'

The old man was blind, and so said, 'Bring the Russian hero that I may greet him!'

Ilya, meanwhile, had warmed the piece of iron, and when he came to give the old man his hand in greeting, he extended the iron in its place. And when the old man grasped it in his mighty hands, he said, 'Your hands are firm, Ilya. You are a most mighty warrior.'

After this, as Svyatogor and his younger brother Ilya journeyed among the Holy Mountains, they came across a big oak tree beside which was a great tomb built of stone. Upon the tomb were written these words: 'This tomb will fit him who is destined to lie in it.'

Ilya decided to test its size, but for him the tomb was both too long and too wide so at once he sprang out of it. But when the giant hero Svyatogor lay in it, it fitted him perfectly. Then the hero spoke these words: 'The tomb was destined for me; take its lid now, Ilya, and cover me.'

But Ilya answered, 'I will not take up the tomb's lid, elder brother, neither will I cover you. Behold, this is no mere jest that you make, attempting to entomb yourself.'

Svyatogor himself took the lid and covered himself up in the tomb with it. But when he tried to lift the lid off again, he could not move it, even though he struggled and strained with all his might. He called to Ilya: 'O my younger brother! It is clear that my fate has sought me out. I cannot raise the lid. Try yourself now to lift it.'

Ilya of Murom tried hard to raise the cover but could not. Then said Svyatogor the hero: 'Take my great battle sword of steel and strike across the lid of the tomb.'

But Ilya's strength was not enough to lift the sword and he was forced to say, 'I cannot lift your sword, O my brother.'

So Svyatogor called to him from within, 'My little brother, bend yourself down to this small chink in the tomb, and I will breathe upon you the spirit of a hero.'

Ilya bent down to the chink and Svyatogor the hero breathed upon him his hero's spirit. Ilya felt that his former strength had become three times as great as before. He now took the sword of steel and struck a blow across the lid of the tomb. Sparks flashed from that blow, but where the great weapon struck a band of iron sprang forth.

The hero Svyatogor called to him again, saying, 'My younger brother, I am suffocating. Try once more, but this time strike lengthwise along the lid with my mighty sword.'

Ilya did as he was instructed, but again where he struck another band of iron sprang forth. Yet again spoke Svyatogor, 'O younger brother, I die. Bend down now to the chink. Yet once more will I breathe upon you, and give you all my vast strength!'

But again Ilya answered thus: 'My strength is sufficient, elder brother; had I more, Earth could not bear me.'

'You have done well, young brother,' said the hero Svyatogor, 'in refusing to do my last bidding. For I should have breathed upon you the breath of death, and you would have fallen dead beside me. But now, fare you well; take my great battle sword of steel, but bind my good heroic steed to this venerable oak tree near my tomb. None save Svyatogor must own that horse.'

Then a dying breath fluttered through the chink. Ilya took leave of the hero Svyatogor, girded himself with his battle sword of steel, but left the heroic beast tethered to the oak near its master's tomb, and he rode away into the free and open plain.

And Svyatogor's burning tears flow through the tomb evermore.

Baldak Borisievich

Many Russian stories tell of extraordinary exploits at a very young age: in some of the saints' stories, they are described as practising asceticism at just three years of age.

Valiant Prince Vladimir called together the dukes, nobles and mighty heroes of royal Kiev in his castle for a solemn feast. The prince spoke these words: 'Greetings, my faithful subjects! Assemble yourselves beside me and let us sit down together at one table.' They gathered thus at one table, ate and drank half their fill, when Vladimir spoke again, 'Which one of you will render me a great service? Who will go beyond thrice-nine lands to the thrice-tenth kingdom, to the Tatar sultan, and capture his good steed with the golden mane, butcher his talking cat, and spit in the sultan's own face?' The bold knight Ilya of Murom, son of Ivan, immediately volunteered to go. But the beloved daughter of Prince Vladimir, the Princess Anastasia, gave a warning to her father: 'My father, Prince Vladimir, Ilya of Murom merely boasts aloud; he will not accomplish this task. Dismiss your guests, O father, and go to all the taverns of royal Kiev. Seek out the young Baldak, son of Boris, just seven years of age.'

The prince agreed to do as his daughter instructed, and set out to find the young Baldak Borisievich. He discovered the lad in a drinking house, sleeping under a bench. The prince prodded him roughly with the sharp toe of his boot and instantly Baldak woke up and jumped to his feet, as if nothing had happened. 'Greetings, Prince Vladimir, what is it that you require of me?'

'I invite you to an honourable feast at my castle,' answered Prince Vladimir.

'But I am not worthy to attend such an event; I frequent taverns, become drunk and wallow on the floor.'

'If I invite you to an honourable feast, Baldak Borisievich, you have no choice,' said Vladimir firmly. 'Indeed,' he added, 'you must come because I have great need of you.'

'Leave me alone for the moment, O Prince,' replied young Baldak the drunkard. 'Return to your royal castle, and I promise I will follow you before too long.'

Baldak, staying behind in the drinking house, needed to revive himself. He drank enough green wine to chase away his inebriation, and then set off without delay to Prince Vladimir's royal castle. Upon entering the hall, he crossed himself as was prescribed, bowed low as has been taught, and inclined his head to all sides as was enjoined, especially to the prince himself.

'Greetings, your Majesty,' he said. 'Why have you invited me to this celebration?'

'Young Baldak Borisievich,' Prince Vladimir exclaimed, 'render me a great service. Go beyond the thrice-nine lands to the thrice-tenth kingdom and present yourself to the Tatar sultan. Take from him his good steed with the golden mane, butcher his talking cat, and spit in the sultan's own face. You may take with you as many men-at-arms as you require, and as much gold and bounty as you please.'

'I am at your command, Prince Vladimir,' answered young Baldak Borisievich. 'For my troops I want only twenty-nine youths; I myself will be the thirtieth.'

Young Baldak Borisievich and his companions set out to the kingdom of the Tatars. They journeyed for a long time or a short time (for a tale may be spun with speed, but less speedily is a deed accomplished) and managed to reach their destination at midnight. Baldak forced his way into the sultan's courtyard, stole the good steed with the golden mane, seized the talking cat and split him into two with his sabre, and spat in the sultan's own face while he slept.

Now the Tatar sultan happened to have a favourite garden which covered an area of one hundred acres. In this garden all kinds of tree were planted and all types of flowers grew. Baldak Borisievich gave orders to those in his command, the twenty-nine youths, to destroy the entire garden, cut down every tree and flower and set it on fire. The blaze enveloped every inch of the garden and razed everything to the ground. In the area where the garden had once been, Baldak pitched thirty thin white canvas tents.

The next day, at first light, the Tatar sultan arose and, as was his custom, he went to his bedroom balcony to look out over his favourite garden. To his horror he saw that all the trees and flowers had been cut and burned, and that thirty thin white canvas tents stood where the garden had been. 'What manner of man has trespassed upon my garden?' he thought. 'An emperor, a king, or a most powerful hero?' Angry and bitter, the sultan cried out in a loud voice for his faithful Tatar pasha.

'My kingdom is under threat,' he said to the pasha. 'I have been waiting for some Russian villain, the treacherous Baldak Borisievich, but now I have been invaded – by whom? An emperor, a king, or a most powerful hero? I do not know, nor do I know how to find out.'

The sultan called for his advisers to discuss a strategy. But his eldest daughter came up to him and said, 'O great Tatar sultan, my father! Why have you called for your advisers; what is it that you wish to learn but cannot? Bestow upon me your blessing and command that twenty-nine maidens, the most beautiful in the whole kingdom, be chosen. I myself will be the thirtieth. Together we shall go to those white canvas tents by night, find the evil-doer, and deliver him to you.'

Her father did not wish her to go, but he knew no other way to find the malefactor, so he reluctantly agreed. That evening she went to the tents with twenty-nine maidens, the most beautiful in the whole kingdom. Young Baldak Borisievich was taken by surprise at their coming. He went out to greet the sultan's daughter, took her by her white hands, and called out in a loud voice, 'Approach, brave comrades! Take each one of you a lovely maiden by her hands, and show good Russian hospitality.'

A great celebration was held and there was much merriment and carousing throughout the night. The next morning the sultan's eldest daughter came back to him and said, 'O great Tatar sultan, my father, invite the thirty Russian youths from the thin white canvas tents to come to the palace; I myself will identify the man who destroyed your garden.'

Without delay, the Tatar sultan despatched his favourite pasha to the tents to invite young Baldak Borisievich and all his companions to the royal palace. The thirty young men emerged from their tents: they were all of one face, like blood brothers, hair for hair, voice for voice, eyes for eyes. And as one man they replied to the pasha, 'Go back to your sultan; we shall follow you in due course.'

Then young Baldak Borisievich asked his comrades, 'Is there perchance some mark or sign on my body? Look me over carefully.'

To their surprise they found that his legs were smeared with gold up to the knees, and his arms with silver up to the elbows. 'How devious the princess is,' said Baldak, 'but I know what she is up to.' And he set about putting the same colours on the limbs of all his companions: their legs were now gold up to the knees and their arms silver up to the elbows. In addition, he commanded that they all wear gloves. 'No one must remove his gloves in the palace of the sultan without an instruction from me.'

They arrived at the Tatar palace and entered. Straight away the eldest daughter stepped forward and pointed her finger at young Baldak Borisievich. 'Here is the culprit,' she said to her father, the sultan.

'How do you know it was me?' asked Baldak. 'What proof do you have?'

'Remove your boots from your legs and your gloves from your hands,' commanded the Tatar princess, 'for I have placed my mark. Your legs are gold up to the knees and your arms silver up to the elbows.'

'Is there not more than one of our company like this?' asked young Baldak Borisievich, and shouted an order to his men: 'Everyone now remove a boot from one leg and a glove from one hand!' And behold, the same colours were smeared on all the Russians, to the extent that the sultan's room was illuminated by the glow from the silver and gold.

Seeing this, the sultan showed mercy to Baldak and his troop, but was highly vexed with his daughter. 'You are a liar,' he declared accusingly. 'I need one guilty man, but now, according to you, there are thirty.' Then he dismissed everyone and slammed the door in disgust and confusion.

The sultan's distress and annoyance had only been made worse by these events, so again he began to ponder the situation and to seek counsel from the court advisers and his favourite pasha. Another meeting was called the following day to discuss how to locate the malefactor.

Then came the sultan's second daughter and said to him, 'O great Tatar sultan, my father! Bestow upon me your blessing and command that twenty-nine beautiful maidens be chosen. I myself will be the thirtieth. Together we shall go to the white canvas tents by night, find the evil doer, and deliver him to you.'

Again her father reluctantly agreed and the second daughter went to the tents with the twenty-nine maidens, and spent a merry evening there. In due course, as before, the Tatar sultan despatched his favourite pasha to the tents to invite young Baldak

Borisievich and all his companions to the royal palace. As before, they replied unanimously, 'Go back to your sultan; we shall follow you in due course,'

With the pasha's departure, young Baldak called to his comrades, 'Approach me, my friends and brothers, you twenty-nine lads! Search my body diligently to discover whether or not there is some sign or mark.' To their amazement they discovered golden hair on his head. 'This one is also very devious,' said Baldak, 'but it is not difficult to see what she is up to.' He set about putting golden hair on the heads of all his companions, just as had been done to him, and commanded that they cover their turbulent heads with a cap. 'No one must remove his cap in the palace of the sultan without an instruction from me,' he ordered.

They arrived at the Tatar palace and entered, and immediately the sultan said to his second daughter, 'My beloved daughter, show me the guilty one.' And believing that she knew with certainty who it was, she walked straight up to young Baldak, pointing her accusing finger, 'Here is the culprit; the destroyer of gardens.'

'How do you know it was me?' responded Baldak Borisievich. 'Do you have any proof?'

'Remove the cap from your head,' commanded the Tatar princess, 'for I have placed my mark on your head – golden hair.'

'Is there not more than one of our company like this?' answered Baldak, taking off his cap. He then turned to his men and shouted an order: 'Everyone now remove his cap!'

Seeing this, the sultan grew furious with his second daughter: 'How could you lie to me like this? You are no better than your elder sister. I need one guilty man but now, according to you, all thirty are guilty.' Then he dismissed everyone, as before, in total disgust and confusion.

At last, the sultan's third and youngest daughter approached him. She ridiculed her two elder sisters and besought her father's blessing. 'O great Tatar sultan, my father! Allow me to select twenty-nine beautiful maidens, the loveliest in the kingdom; I myself will be the thirtieth. Together we shall go to those white canvas tents by night, find the evil doer, and deliver him to you.'

Reluctantly her father agreed and she went to the same tents with twenty-nine beautiful maidens, the loveliest in the kingdom. Young Baldak Borisievich was taken by surprise at their coming. He went out to greet the sultan's daughter, took her by her white hands, and called out in a loud voice, 'Approach, brave comrades! Take each one of you a lovely maiden by her hands, and show good Russian hospitality.' After a night of celebrating and carousing, the princess and the maidens returned home.

Once again the sultan despatched his favourite pasha to the tents to invite young Baldak Borisievich and all his companions to the royal palace. 'Go back to your sultan; we shall follow you in due course,' was the united response.

Then young Baldak asked his comrades, 'Well, my friends and brothers, do as you did before. Look me over carefully to discover whether or not there is some sign or mark.' They examined and searched all over his body but failed to detect any mark or sign. 'Woe to us, my brothers, for surely I am now defeated.' And Baldak requested them to render him a final service. He handed them each a sharp sabre which they were to hide under their garments. 'And when I give the signal,' he instructed, 'cut in all directions.'

They arrived at the Tatar palace and when they entered the sultan's youngest daughter drew near and pointed her accusing finger at young Baldak. 'This is the guilty one,' she answered, 'for he has a golden star under his heel.' And indeed there was a golden star under his heel, just as she had said, which had remained undetected by the heroes.

Now the sultan dismissed all twenty-nine youths from the palace, and detained only the culprit, young Baldak Borisievich. In a loud and threatening voice he cried, 'I will seize you, place you on the palm of one hand, and flatten you like a pancake with the other! Nothing will be left of you but a damp spot!'

'O Tatar sultan,' answered the captive bravely, 'emperors, kings and mighty heroes may fear you, but I, a seven-year-old boy, do not. It was I who stole your steed with the golden mane, butchered your talking cat, spat in your own face, and cut and burned the trees and flowers in your favourite garden!' The sultan flew into an uncontrollable rage and commanded his attendants to clear the city square and erect two columns of oak with a maplewood cross-beam. On this crossbeam they were to suspend three nooses – the first of silk, the second of hemp, and the third of bast. This done, the sultan circulated an edict throughout the city, that ordered everyone, both great and small, to assemble on the square and see how the Russian criminal would be punished by death.

The Tatar sultan, his youngest daughter, who had identified Baldak, and the pasha rode to the square in a white carriage drawn by four black horses. At the rear of the carriage young Baldak was bound, chained and blindfolded. On the way to the oaken column young Baldak addressed the Tatar sultan: 'By your leave, O sultan, allow me to speak three sayings which I invite you to interpret. A horse runs fast; why does its tail drag?'

'What a stupid riddle,' replied the sultan. 'Every horse is born with a tail.'

They rode a little farther and Baldak spoke again, 'We know that the horses drive the carriage's front wheels, but what on earth makes the back wheels turn?'

'What a simpleton! His approaching execution has made the Russian lose all reason; he is totally confused. The carriage-maker made the four wheels; hence four wheels turn.'

Upon arriving at the square everyone got out of the carriage and the victim was untied and unchained. He was then led to the gallows and they removed his blindfold so he could see and choose his noose. Young Baldak son of Boris, made the sign of the cross, bowed low to all sides, and called out in a loud voice, 'O Tatar sultan, before you give the order to have me hanged, may I be granted a final wish?'

'Speak up; what is it?'

'I have a gift left to me by my dead father and a blessing from my mother. It is a Kievan horn of brass. Allow me to play on it one last time.' Permission was granted and Baldak produced a merry tune, a captivating air that drew everybody's attention. All men, women and children in that square concentrated their attention on this expert horn player whose flashing eyes and nimble steps clouded their minds and left them speechless. None could remember the reason for their being there and even the sultan was struck dumb. At the horn's first notes, the twenty-nine brave Russian youths moved in from the rear and began to cut down all the citizens with their sharp sabres. More and more intensely did Baldak play, holding the crowd's attention, until the rattling sabres had finished off everyone as far as the gallows.

Then Baldak Borisievich stopped his playing and gave the Tatar sultan his third saying: 'Now who is the simpleton? Take a look behind you; turn around! My geese have pecked your wheat.'

Regaining his senses, the sultan turned around and saw that all his subjects had been slain and were lying in piles on the ground. The only three that were left – himself, his youngest daughter and the pasha – were standing ominously at the gallows. Young Baldak commanded his youths to hang the sultan with the silken noose, his favourite pasha with the hemp noose and his youngest daughter with the noose of bast. This completed, Baldak Borisievich and his brave comrades departed for the royal city of Kiev, to return to Prince Vladimir himself.

Dobrynya Nikitich and the Dragon

Young Dobrynya Nikitich, the knight, took up his stout, death-dealing bow, his fiery little arrows, and set off to hunt by the Blue Sea. At the first cove he found neither geese, nor swans, nor small grey ducks. Neither did he find them at the second or third coves. Then Dobrynya's restive heart grew hot within him; he turned back quickly and went to his home, to his widowed mother, Afimya Alexandrevna. He sat down in the banquet hall upon the square hewn bench, and cast his eyes down towards the oaken floor. His mother came to him, and said 'Ho, young Dobrynya Nikitich. You have come back in a most miserable mood!'

'Ah, my mother,' he said, 'there was no joy in my hunting. Give me your leave and blessing to go to the Puchai River.'

'Young Dobrynya,' replied his mother, 'I shall give you neither leave nor blessing. For none who has gone to the Puchai River has ever returned from that fearful place.'

'Ah, sweet mother,' said Dobrynya, 'whether or not you give me your leave and blessing, I shall go.'

So Afimya Alexandrevna consented. Dobrynya threw off his embroidered cloak and put on garments fit for a journey. He took a tunic of calf hide with red satin sleeves, and a mantle made from the yellow and black skins of three Libyan tigers. A Moroccan belt was strapped round his waist, its gleaming gold buckle encrusted with three blue sapphires. His feet were clothed in seven silks, and on his head was a wide brimmed hat from the queen of cities, Constantinople – a hat such as a Christian priest might wear. Then he saddled and bridled a good steed which no man but he had ever ridden, took his stout bow, his fiery arrows, his sharp sword and far-reaching spear, and his battle mace.

As he rode forth, accompanied by his young page, Semyon, his mother issued her final instructions: 'If you must go to the Puchai River, young Dobrynya, immense heat will overcome you. Even so, do not bathe in the waters of Mother Puchai, for she is fierce and angry. From her first stream leap tongues of fire; from her second fly showers of sparks; and from her third rise clouds of suffocating smoke.'

When he came to the Puchai River, intolerable heat overpowered him, and he did not heed his mother's warnings. From his head he removed his hat from Constantinople, took off his tunic of calf hide, his mantle of tiger skins and his footwear of the seven silks, and began to bathe in the Puchai.

'Afimya Alexandrevna said this was a wild and cruel stream,' he said, 'but it is gentle and as peaceful as a pool of rainwater.' He dived like a duck beneath the first stream, and through the second likewise. But he was astonished to see that, where there was no wind, the clouds sailed on; where there were no clouds, the rain fell down; where there was no rain, yet the lightning flashed; where there was no lightning, yet sparks showered fast. What obscured the sky was not thick darkness, not forbidding clouds descending, but a ferocious dragon flying down upon Dobrynya, the savage Dragon of the Cavern, with her twelve tails.

'Aha, young Dobrynya Nikitich,' said the dragon. 'Now I shall devour you whole. I shall carry you back to my deep cave where you shall perish.'

'Ho, you accursed dragon,' cried Dobrynya, 'Do your boasting only when you have captured Dobrynya. For the moment I am well out of reach and I intend to remain that way!' Then he dived swiftly beneath the first stream, out through the second, and emerged naked from the third. But his young page, Semyon, had been over-hasty and had sent off Dobrynya's good steed. He had taken away the stout bow, the sharp sword, the far-reaching spear, the battle-mace and all the clothes. The hat alone was left, the wide-brimmed hat from Constantinople.

Dobrynya seized this Christian priest's hat. And because Dobrynya was a knight of Holy Russia, in his hands this hat became an invincible weapon against the powers of darkness and evil. Indeed, when Dobrynya tried to lift this sacred object from Moist Mother Earth, he found that it was extraordinarily heavy. He filled it with earth and smote the cursed worm, hewing off three of her tails.

Thereupon the Dragon of the Cavern besought Dobrynya: 'Ho, young Dobrynya Nikitich! Do not give me over to fruitless death, shed not my innocent blood. I vow never again to fly over Holy Russia, neither shall I imprison her heroes, nor strangle young maidens, nor orphan little children. I shall be forever subject unto you; and you, Dobrynya, shall be my elder brother, and I your younger sister.'

Dobrynya was taken with her wiles and drew back, as she requested. He returned home to his mother and sat down upon the square hewn bench in the banquet hall.

But no sooner had he gone than the cunning dragon raised herself upon her wings and flew over royal Kiev. She circled round and saw Princess Beauty, niece to valiant Prince Vladimir, walking in the palace gardens. The sky was black with her wings as she swooped down on the terrified princess, caught her up between her jaws, and bore her off to the dragon's cave in the hills.

As soon as he learnt of this, valiant Vladimir summoned many princes, nobles, knights, mighty heroes and wandering good youths, and invited them to an honourable feast. Dobrynya sought his mother's leave and blessing to go that feast.

'No,' she answered, 'I shall give you neither leave nor blessing. Stay rather in your own dwelling, Dobrynya, with your mother. Drink red wine until you are full, and spend your golden treasure as your heart wills. But go not to this feast.'

'Ah, sweet mother,' said Dobrynya, 'whether or not you give me your leave and blessing, I shall go.'

So Afimya Alexandrevna consented and Dobrynya arrayed himself as was fitting for an honourable feast in the palace. On his feet he placed shoes of green moroccan leather with high heels and pointed toes. The ends were so sharp that an egg would have been able to roll around them; under the heel sparrows would have been able to fly. His garments were of embroidered gold and his mantle of black sables from beyond the sea.

Dobrynya saddled his good steed and rode forth to the grand court. When he arrived, he tied his horse in the centre, to the ring of gold in the carved pillar, and entered the banquet hall. There he crossed himself as it is prescribed; he made low bows as it is enjoined, to two, three and four sides, and to the prince and princess in particular. Then they led him to the place of honour at the great oaken table, with its savoury meats and honeyed drinks, and poured him a mighty cup of red wine, measuring a bucket and a half, and weighing sixty pounds. This Dobrynya grasped in one hand, and drained at one draught. Then they poured a second cupful of kvas, and a third of sweet mead. Each time Dobrynya raised it with one hand, and drained it in a single draught.

Valiant Vladimir the Prince, pacing the banquet hall and stroking his black curls, looked on the heroes and spoke these words: 'Ho, you brave and mighty heroes! I will lay upon you a great service. You must go to the Tugy Mountains, to the fierce dragon that has carried off our royal niece, Beauty the Fair.'

Then the great hid behind the lesser, and they, in turn, hid behind the small, and from the least in rank no answer came. But from one corner spoke Semyon, the page: 'Little father! Vladimir of royal Kiev! Only yesterday in the open plain I beheld Dobrynya beside the Puchai River in battle with that same dragon. And the dragon beguiled him, calling him her elder brother, herself his younger sister. Send Dobrynya, therefore, to the Tugy Mountains for Princess Beauty.'

So Vladimir laid his commands on Dobrynya; and Dobrynya lamented and was heavy-hearted. He sprang to his nimble feet, in his place within the marble palace, and stamped upon the oaken floor. The tables rocked, the liquor quivered in the glasses, and the heroes were thrown out of their seats from the shock. Dobrynya raced into the courtyard, loosened his good steed from the golden ring, mounted and rode to his own dwelling. When he had spread fine Turkish wheat before the horse in the middle of the courtyard, he entered the house and went to his mother. There in the banquet hall he sat upon the stone hewn bench and hung his turbulent head.

'Why are you so sad?' enquired his mother. 'Was your place at the feast not to your liking or inappropriate to your rank? Did the cup pass you by? Did some boorish drunk spit in your eye, or did the fair damsels scoff at you?'

'Mine was the place of honour at the feast,' Dobrynya answered, 'the greatest place, not the least; no wine passed me by, no fool offended me, no damsel scoffed. But Prince Vladimir has requested of me a heavy task. I must go to the Tugy Mountains and free his niece, the Princess Beauty, from the cruel dragon of the Cavern.'

'Do not grieve,' spoke his mother, the honourable widow, Afimya Alexandrevna. 'Lie down to sleep early this evening. Tomorrow will be wise, for the morning is wiser than the evening.' Her son heeded her; and the next morning, rising early, he washed himself very white and clean, and arrayed himself for the journey.

'Do not be disheartened,' said his mother softly, 'your father, and his father before him, went to the dread Tugy Mountains and slew repulsive serpents; and now you must likewise go thither. But do not take your swift stout bow, or your battle-mace, or even your sharp sword. Instead, I will give you a whip of seven silks from Samarkand. This you must brandish, for it has magic properties. I will also give you this enchanted kerchief. When your right hand begins to falter, and the light begins to fade from your eyes; when the dragon starts to drag you to her lair, and the little dragons bite your horse's hooves as he tramples them, then you must take your enchanted kerchief, lift it to your white face and wipe your clear eyes. Immediately you shall be stronger than before. Draw then this whip, braided from seven silks, from your pocket, and beat your good steed between its ears and on its hind legs. At this, your horse will begin to prance and, shaking off the dragon's brood, will crush them to the last one. Then brandish the silken whip and with it you shall force the dragon to earth and subdue it beneath your feet like a Christian beast; and you shall sever her remaining tails, giving her speedily over to the hands of death.'

So Dobrynya mounted his good steed and rode to the Tugy Mountains and to the dragon's cave. For twelve days he rode, and ate nothing but a wheaten roll. On the thirteenth day he came to the dreaded hills, but the dragon was not in her cave and the royal princess was nowhere to be seen. As he searched here and there, the little dragons began to coil about his horse's hooves as it trampled, so that the brave animal could no longer leap. Dobrynya drew from his pocket the magic whip of the silks of Samarkand and beat the good steed between the ears and on its hind legs. At once the beast began to prance and shake off the dragon brood, crushing them to the very last one.

Gazing out over the open plain, Dobrynya observed the vile serpent flying towards him, clutching the dead body of a hero in her dreadful talons. When she spotted him, the dragon released the hero's body, which fell upon Moist Mother Earth. Then she flew straight at Dobrynya.

'Ho, miserable Dobrynya Nikitich! Why have you broken your oath and crushed all my little babies?'

'And you, accursed dragon,' replied Dobrynya, 'What possessed you to enter royal Kiev and seize the young Princess Beauty? Deliver her now or prepare for battle and bloodshed.

'Without battle or bloodshed I will not deliver Vladimir's royal niece.'

So they waged a mighty battle for a full day until nightfall. For three whole days they fought, but Dobrynya could not defeat the vile monster. At the end of the third day, his right hand began to falter, the light began to fade from his eyes, and the dragon started to drag him towards her lair. Recalling his mother's advice, Dobrynya wiped his clear eyes and his white face upon the kerchief she had given him, and his strength became greater than ever before. Nonetheless, the might of the Dragon also increased and once again she began to gain the ascendancy over him. Just as he was about to surrender, a voice rang out from the skies: 'Brave Dobrynya, fight for another three hours and you shall overcome the beast.' So Dobrynya summoned his courage and his failing strength, and fought on against the dreadful beast. And, as the voice had promised, at long last he succeeded in killing the monster.

But now a new danger threatened. The dragon's blood poured from her body and spread far and wide. Dobrynya waited for the blood to soak away, but Mother Earth would not drink the evil dragon's blood, and closed her mouth against it. Dobrynya found himself marooned in a huge lake of blood and could feel that he was quickly sinking. But the voice spoke yet again from the skies:

'Brave Dobrynya, remain steadfast for yet three more hours. Take your far-reaching spear, smite it upon Moist Mother Earth, and command her: "Gape, O Moist Mother Earth; gape in all four corners! Consume the blood of the dragon!"'

When Dobrynya did this, a huge hole appeared in the ground and swallowed up the filthy flood. Recalling his mother's counsel, Dobrynya drew forth his whip of the seven silks of Samarkand, hewed off the dragon's remaining nine tails, cut the sinuous body into small pieces, and scattered them over Mother Earth.

After that, he entered the dragon's deep den and released those held captive – Russian tsars, princes and nobles by the score, and lesser folk by the thousands – and sent them off to their homes in peace. But young Beauty, the princess, was nowhere to be seen. Deeper and deeper into the cave Dobrynya searched, until he entered the farthest den. There she lay, chained, with arms outstretched. He released her immediately, and led her forth to the white world. He mounted his good steed, and setting Beauty upon it in front of him, rode out over the plain.

'For this great service,' said Beauty, 'I would desire to call you little father, but this I cannot do. For this great deed, I would willingly call you my own brother, but now I may not. Gladly I would call you friend, even my beloved, but you love me not, dear Dobrynya.'

To this Dobrynya made answer: 'Ah, Princess Beauty! You are of royal birth and I am but a humble knight. It is not possible for you to call me friend or beloved.' Realizing the truth of this, the princess was silent.

As they thus rode over the open plain, they came upon the tracks of a horse that had kicked up large clods of earth; so large that one might sink in the hollows as far as the knee. Dobrynya followed the tracks, and by the side of the trail he came across Alyosha Popovich, the priest's son.

'Ho there, Alyosha Popovich,' he cried, 'take the Princess Beauty and bear her in honour to Vladimir, our Fair Sun Prince in royal Kiev. Fail me in this and you stand to lose your turbulent head.' This Alyosha accomplished. And so Dobrynya rescued Beauty and sent her safely home.

Dobrynya continued to follow the the giant tracks and before long he spied in the distance a knight in the open plain. The knight was dressed in woman's garb and riding upon a fair and sturdy horse.

'Ah,' said Dobrynya, 'this is no hero, but a mighty wandering damsel, someone's maid or wife.' He then rode after the mounted damsel and struck her upon her turbulent head with his battle-mace of damascened steel. But the warlike maiden sat still on her sturdy beast, neither wavering nor glancing back. Dobrynya started back in horror and retreated from that place. 'It is clear,' he said, 'that Dobrynya's valour may not be lacking, but his strength is not the strength of earlier days!'

Now there stood nearby in the plain, an oak six fathoms in girth. Dobrynya smote it with his mace and reduced it to splinters; and he marvelled greatly. 'It is true,' he said, 'Dobrynya's might is as of old, but his courage is not the courage of earlier days.'

Then he rode again in pursuit of the bold virgin warrior and again struck her honourably upon her turbulent head. As before, she neither wavered nor glanced behind. But Dobrynya was altogether amazed; he tested his might upon a huge oak of twelve fathoms and split it into shreds. Dobrynya's anger mounted as he sat on his good steed. He rode after the bold virgin warrior a third time and struck her with his mace.

At this she turned and spoke: 'I thought the Russian gnats were biting; but look, it's the Russian hero tapping!'

Then she seized Dobrynya by his golden curls, twisted him from his horse, dropped him into her deep leather pouch, and rode away over the open plain. At length, her good steed spoke: 'Ho, young Nastasya, daughter of Mikula, bold warrior maid! I cannot carry two heroes. That knight you hold has might equal to yours; and his courage is twice your own.'

Young Nastasya replied: 'If this hero be very aged, I will cut off his head. If he be young and handsome, I will call him friend and beloved. If he pleases me not, I will place him on my left palm and squash him with my right, and make a pancake of him.'

With these words she drew him forth from the leather pouch and admired him greatly. 'Greetings, dear Dobrynya Nikitich,' she cried.

'How is that you know of me, bold virgin knight? For I know you not.'

'In Kiev, the royal city, I have often seen you. But how could you know me? I am daughter to the Polish king and my name is Nastasya Mikulichna. I spend my days roaming the open plain, seeking an adversary. If you will accept my hand in marriage, Dobrynya, I shall grant you your life. Moreover, you must take a solemn oath, and if you refuse I shall make an oatcake out of you.'

'Grant me my life, young Nastasya, for I will take that solemn oath and I will also take the golden crown with you.'

So they made their oaths and set out for Kiev, to valiant Prince Vladimir. Dobrynya's mother came out to meet them and enquired, 'Who have you there, Dobrynya Nikitich?'

'Ah, Afimya Alexandrevna, my honourable widowed mother! I bring my adversary, the young Nastasya Mikulichna. I fought her on the plain, but I could not prevail against her. With her shall I take the golden crown in marriage.'

Then they went to Prince Vladimir and entered the royal banquet hall, where Dobrynya made the prescribed bows to all, and especially to the prince and princess.

'Hail, Fair Sun Vladimir of royal Kiev!'

'Hail, Dobrynya Nikitich! Who have you there?'

Thereupon Dobrynya told him of all the events. Nastasya was received into the Christian faith, and they took the golden marriage crowns. Valiant Prince Vladimir honoured them with a great feast that lasted three days and thereafter they lived most happily.

Alyosha Popovich

In the heavens was born a bright new moon, and on earth, to the house of old Leontii, the priest of Rostov Cathedral, was born a son, a mighty hero. They named him Alyosha Popovich, a very fine name, and they fed him on meat and drink. In one day he grew as much as other infants grow in a week; in one week he was like other infants at the end of a year. Before long he learned to walk, wander the streets, and play with other little children. But when he grasped someone by the arm, that arm came off; if he grasped someone by the foot, that foot came off – so cruel were his games. Once he even grabbed a man round the waist and pulled out his belly!

Time passed and Alyosha came of age. 'Give me your blessing,' he asked his father and mother. 'Allow me to seek my fortune and do battle in the open plains.'

'Beware, my son Alyosha,' warned his father, 'for on the field of battle there are mightier men than you. Take with you, therefore, young Akim Ivanovich as your faithful steward, and go with my blessing.'

Thus the two mighty heroes rode forth from glorious Rostov, like two bright falcons soaring. Shoulder to shoulder they rode, stirrup pressed to heroic stirrup. Roaming over the open plain, they saw nothing stir, no bird flying overhead, no beast fleet of foot.

But soon they espied before them three broad roads in that plain, and standing at their junction a burning stone with writing carved on it. Then spoke up young Alyosha: 'My brother Akim Ivanovich, you have been instructed in letters and script. Look now upon these words carved in the stone and interpret for me the meaning.'

So Akim leaped from his good steed and read the writing on the stone. It told of the three broad roads and their destinations. 'The first road leads to Murom, the second to the city of Chernigov, and the third to royal Kiev and the court of valiant Prince Vladimir.

'Now, my brother, young Alyosha Popovich. Along which road do you wish to ride?' asked Akim.

And young Alyosha answered, 'It will be best for us to go to royal Kiev, to valiant Prince Vladimir.' So they wheeled their good steeds about, and took the third road to the city of Kiev.

When they reached the Safat River, they paused in the green meadows to feed the noble steeds. There they pitched two white tents, for Alyosha was very tired. And when young Akim had hobbled the good steeds and set them free to graze in the green meadow, he too lay down in his own tent to seek repose.

The autumn night passed. Alyosha awoke from sleep at the first light, rose, washed himself in the dews of dawn, dried himself with a white towel, and turned to the east to pray to God. Then young Akim went quickly after their good steeds and led them to drink in the streams of the Safat River, for Alyosha had commanded him to saddle the horses with speed; and when this was done they mounted and made ready to go to the city of Kiev.

As they rode, there came to them a wandering pilgrim. His feet were shod in seven silks, soled with pure silver, and their tops were studded with red gold. His long mantle was of sable; his hat was from the Grecian lands, and at his side were a travelling whip weighing one thousand pounds and a cudgel moulded of heaviest lead weighing twice as much. He spoke these words: 'Greetings, bold and goodly youths! I have seen Tugarin, the Dragon's son. His height exceeds three fathoms and between his sloping shoulders is a span of one fathom. The space between his eyes is an arrow's length; the horse beneath him resembles a ferocious wild beast, for from his jaws pour burning flames and from his ears issues a column of smoke.'

Young Alyosha struck a bargain with him: 'Good wanderer, give me your pilgrim garb and take instead my heroic raiment. I have need of your footwear of seven silks, their soles of pure silver and their tops studded with red gold. I desire your long mantle of sable, your hat from the Grecian lands, the heavy whip and leaden cudgel.' The pilgrim did not refuse, but gave his garments to

Alyosha and dressed himself in heroic garb. Alyosha quickly arrayed himself as a wandering pilgrim, with the thousand-pound whip and a dagger of damascened steel in case of need. Taking himself to the Safat River he caught sight of young Tugarin, the Dragon's son, roaring in a raucous voice. The green oaks trembled and Alyosha Popovich could not bear the sound of that roar.

'Listen, wandering pilgrim,' demanded Tugarin, 'Have you heard or seen traces anywhere of young Alyosha Popovich? For I long to thrust him through with my lance and burn him with fire.'

Then the disguised Alyosha answered, 'Greetings, young Tugarin, Dragon's son! Come closer, for I cannot hear what you say.' Young Tugarin the Dragon's son came up and stood before Alyosha. Immediately Alyosha set on Tugarin, brandished his staff round his head and smote a mighty blow on Tugarin's turbulent head, cracking it open. Tugarin fell down upon Moist Mother Earth while Alyosha sprang upon his enemy's black beast.

'Ho, wandering pilgrim,' besought young Tugarin. 'Are you not Alyosha Popovich? If indeed you are him, let us now swear brotherhood together. Let us take an oath.'

But Alyosha did not trust his enemy; he struck him once again, leaving him half dead on Moist Mother Earth. Stripping Tugarin of his patterned garments, which were worth one hundred roubles, he dressed himself in them and set off on his good steed towards the white tent.

Now when Akim saw him coming, he was terribly afraid, for he thought from the robes that it was Tugarin the Dragon's son. Leaping upon his good steed he rode with haste back to Rostov town. Alyosha followed him and overtook him. Seeing this, Akim Ivanovich drew out his battle-mace weighing one thousand pounds and flung it behind him, striking Alyosha Popovich on his white breast and hurling him from his Circassian saddle.

Alyosha fell faint upon Moist Mother Earth. Akim Ivanovich sprang down from his good steed and would have run him through, but then he espied a cross of wondrous gold upon Alyosha's breast.

'Alas!' he cried, lamenting over his comrade's body, 'This thing has come upon me for my sins – that I, Akim, should slay my own brother.' He then began to shake and rock Alyosha. He gave him liquor from beyond the sea, and Alyosha revived and became whole again.

They talked together while Alyosha removed the patterned garments of Tugarin the Dragon's son, placing them in his saddle bag, and put on ordinary clothes. Then they mounted their good steeds and rode off to the glorious city of royal Kiev.

Meanwhile, Tugarin the Dragon's son had recovered from Alyosha's blows. He was so angry at being fooled and robbed by Alyosha that he began to go about the countryside of Kiev pillaging and laying waste the villages.

When the brave knights came to the realm of Prince Vladimir, they got off their horses, tied them to the oaken pillars and entered the fair hall of the white stone palace. There they prayed before the icon of the Saviour, crossed themselves as is prescribed, and bowed as they had been taught: to Prince Vladimir, Princess Apraxia, and on all four sides.

'Welcome, bold knights, sit here beside me at this oaken table; eat and drink your fill,' said the prince. They ate superb gingerbreads, washing them down with heady wines. Vladimir then asked them: 'Who are you, brave youths? Are you bold and mighty champions, or chance travellers? Tell me your names and the names of your fathers.'

Alyosha Popovich answered for both: 'My lord, I am the son of the elder Leontii, the priest of Rostov Cathedral, and am called Alyosha Popovich. Here by my side is my faithful steward and comrade, Akim Ivanovich.'

'Your name is well known to me, good knight, and you are welcome in this place. Take pride of place beside my royal throne; at the second place at the oaken bench; or indeed the third, wheresoever you wish,' said Prince Vladimir cheerfully.

Alyosha Popovich chose neither the first nor the second seats of honour but seated himself on a beam by the brick oven to rest, for it was after midday. Akim Ivanovich remained where he was, at the oaken table. Almost at once a fearsome noise was heard outside, the hall doors were flung open and into the chamber stormed Tugarin the Dragon's son.

This ill-bred, heathen brute neither crossed himself nor bowed to the royal couple, but with one stride of his left leg he crossed the threshold, and with one stride of his right he reached the oaken table. There he ate and drank like a glutton and arrogantly embraced Princess Apraxia. With his huge arms he swept aside the sweetmeats, mead and liquor from beyond the seas, making mockery of Prince Vladimir. Tugarin did not eat his bread with honour but thrust an entire loaf in one cheek – and they were monastery loaves of vast size – and another in the other cheek. Next he put a whole roast swan on his tongue, and pushed it in with a pancake, chewing with massive jaws and fat cheeks bulging. Then he spat the bones out onto the floor.

Tugarin did not drink his wine with honour but gulped a whole cup down in a single draught, and the measure of that cup was a bucket and a half.

Finally bold Alyosha Popovich, who was lying by the brick stove and observing this loathsome behaviour, rose up.

'What ails you Vladimir, great prince of Kiev? What boorish knave is this that comes to your court? Who can tolerate this uncultured fool who sits dishonourably at your table and lays his hand upon the Princess Apraxia, kissing her on her sugar lips and jeering at you, O lord? My father the elder Leontii once had an old dog that dragged himself with immense effort under the banquet table and choked himself on a bone. My father grabbed him by the tail and flung him out of the courtyard. And I shall do the same to Tugarin.'

Tugarin the Dragon's son blackened with rage like a night in autumn, but Alyosha Popovich shone like the bright moon.

The cunning servants, to prevent catastrophe, brought in more savoury foods and wine – even a grand suckling pig which the princess attempted to carve. In so doing she cut her left hand, then wrapped it in her sleeve and let it hang beneath the table. 'O you nobles and heroes!' she said. 'I desired to carve the suckling pig, but my desire is greater to gaze upon this sweet youth, Tugarin the Dragon's son.' As she spoke, Tugarin seized the suckling pig and immediately swallowed it whole along with two more giant loaves.

'Valiant Prince Vladimir!' cried Alyosha. 'What a pathetic and ignoble dullard is this who sits at your table! He consumes whole loaves in his fat cheeks and makes a mouthful of a suckling pig. My father the elder Leontii once had a miserable old cow that dragged herself with immense effort from ale house to ale house drinking entire barrels of beer and their dregs. Then this stupid and greedy cow went to a lake and drank all the water from it. Suddenly she burst. My father grabbed her by the tail and flung her over the hill. And I shall do the same to Tugarin.'

Tugarin the Dragon's son blackened with rage like a night in autumn, pulled out his steel dagger, and flung it at Alyosha. But Alyosha was agile and fleet of foot, and dodged behind an oaken pillar. Quick as a flash, Akim Ivanovich seized the dagger by the hilt as it flew swiftly through the air. He then jumped up from behind the oaken table onto his nimble feet, grabbed Tugarin by the neck, pulled him from the oaken table, and hurled him against the white wall. The windows were shattered in splinters. Akim shouted to Alyosha: 'Take Tugarin's steel knife and throw it at him yourself. Or do you command me to hurl it? For I shall cut open his white breast, dim his bright eyes, and remove his fiery heart.'

'O faithful and devoted brother,' cried Alyosha, 'I will neither cast the blade nor command you to do it. Let us not befoul this white stone palace. Rather, I shall meet him tomorrow in the open field and there do battle. Also, I shall lay a great wager with him – not of a hundred roubles, nor even of a thousand – my turbulent head shall be my stake.'

Then all the nobles and courtiers sprang to their nimble feet and backed Tugarin. The nobles staked a hundred roubles, the courtiers fifty each, and the peasants five. Even the shipping merchants from far-off lands staked on Tugarin all their three vessels and all the foreign merchandise that stood on the swiftly-flowing Dniepr. Alyosha's sole supporter was the duke of Chernigov.

The Princess Apraxia sprang to her nimble feet and began to upbraid Alyosha Popovich: 'You miserable, rustic clod. You who would prevent my sweet friend from staying here!' But Alyosha paid no attention to her words of reproach but arose and hastened forth with his comrade Akim Ivanovich.

They mounted their brave steeds and rode to the Safat River where they pitched their white tents and prepared to rest. All that night Alyosha did not sleep, but besought the Lord with tears: 'Fashion, O God, a threatening cloud, send a cloud with thunder, lightning, rain and hail!' The following day Akim Ivanovich rose at the first light of dawn and led the spirited horses out to drink at the swiftly-flowing stream. High in the heavens above him flew Tugarin, the Dragon's son, mounted on his black steed. He had made himself large paper wings that carried him and his horse through the air. The accursed monster now challenged Alyosha Popovich to meet him on the open field.

And Akim Ivanovich, angry at his comrade, came to him, saying: 'May God be your judge, Alyosha Popovich, for you did not permit me to use the steel knife. I would have cut open Tugarin's white breast, dimmed his bright eyes and removed his fiery heart. But now what can I get from this ogre, for he flies through the air!'

'If I do not triumph,' replied Alyosha, 'heaven is betrayed. Go, Akim, to the white stone palace and await my return.'

Bringing forth his good steed, Alyosha strapped round him a Circassian saddle, tightened it with twelve silken girths (not for beauty's sake, but for strength) and sallied forth to the open field. He crossed the field both this way and that, and beheld Tugarin the Dragon's son soaring above him through the air. Once again Alyosha raised his eyes heavenward and sent up a prayer: 'Holy Mother of God, send forth a black cloud and pelting rain to destroy Tugarin's paper wings!'

The prayers were heard by Christ and His Mother. A threatening black cloud rolled over the sky and a pelting storm fell with mighty force to soak Tugarin's paper wings. They wilted and shredded into small pieces so that he fell like a dog upon Moist Mother Earth. Then Akim came and told Alyosha that he had seen Tugarin stretched out upon the ground; so Alyosha hastily arrayed himself, mounted his good steed, took hold of his sharp sword and rode against Tugarin the Dragon's son in the open field.

Like two mountains rolling together, so did Tugarin and Alyosha meet. They clashed with their maces – which broke at the handles. They dashed with their spears – which twisted at their hilts. They slashed with their sabres – which split in two. Without warning, Alyosha stumbled and fell from his Circassian saddle like a sheaf of oats, and Tugarin began to smite him. The Dragon's son roared in a menacing voice: 'Ho there, young Alyosha Popovich! Shall I burn you with fire, or trample you with my bold steed, or impale you upon my lance?'

But Alyosha was agile and fleet of foot. He dodged under the horse's belly and rolled on Moist Mother Earth under the beast to the other side. He stabbed Tugarin with his knife and wounded his right breast. He forced him down from his black steed and shouted, 'Ho there, young Tugarin the Dragon's son. You laid a great wager with me, to contend and fight in mortal combat; but now there is neither courage nor strength left in you against me. Prepare, then, to meet your end; for I shall cut open your white breast, dim your bright eyes, and remove your fiery heart.'

Instantly, Alyosha sprang upon Tugarin and hewed off his turbulent head. The head fell upon Moist Mother Earth like a beet kettle. Then Alyosha stuck Tugarin's bloody head on the end of his lance and rode back to Prince Vladimir with his trophy. On the way Alyosha toyed and played with the head, throwing it high in the air and balancing it on the point of his lance. Observing this macabre game from afar, Prince Vladimir was full of dread. 'Look there, it is Tugarin the Dragon's son playing with Alyosha's turbulent head,' he cried. 'Now it is certain that he will enslave our Christian kingdom.'

'Do not fear, O prince,' answered Akin Ivanovich, 'for if that monster Tugarin does not fly through the air but rides on Moist Mother Earth, my steel spear will pierce his ugly neck. Rest assured, fair prince. When the right moment comes, I, Akim Ivanovich, will meet Tugarin in battle.'

Then Akim Ivanovich looked through his spyglass and immediately recognized Alyosha Popovich. 'I know him by his heroic posture and his noble gait,' he said to Prince Vladimir. 'See Alyosha wheeling his horse, tossing high the head of Tugarin and balancing it on the point of his lance. No, it is not the scoundrel Tugarin riding yonder, but Alyosha Popovich, the son of elder Leontii, priest of Rostov Cathedral. And on his lance he bears the head of the foul Tugarin the Dragon's son.'

When Alyosha entered the palace courtyard, he flung the miserable head to the ground. Prince Vladimir was seated at a richly decorated table and ordered the banquet to proceed. After the sumptuous meal, Prince Vladimir drew Alyosha aside and spoke thus: 'Ho, young Alyosha Popovich! I am greatly in your debt, for you have brought peace to my kingdom. Abide with us in royal Kiev town, I pray you, and join my noble troop of knights. Give your consent and I shall bestow upon you my heartfelt love and many riches.'

This offer was greatly to Alyosha's liking so he and Akim Ivanovich settled in Kiev and served valiant Prince Vladimir with loyalty and truth. But Princess Apraxia continued in her sorrow: 'You common peasant and disgusting oaf! You have parted me from my dearest friend, young Tugarin the Dragon's son.'

To which Alyosha replied, 'Princess Apraxia, my little mother, I had almost called you then by the name which you deserve.'

Vasili Buslayevich the Brave of Novgorod

In glorious Novgorod the Great dwelt old Buslay; for ninety years he dwelt there. He lived in peace with Novgorod; he did not challenge the men of Pskov; and he had no dispute with Mother Moscow. In this way Buslay lived to a ripe old age until, full of years, he was gathered to his fathers. He left one son and heir, the young and amiable Vasili.

When he had reached his seventh year, his mother, the widow Amalfa Timofeyevna, sent Vasili for instruction in reading and writing. Vasili excelled at his lessons. Then his mother sent him to master the art of church singing, and in all Novgorod the Great there was no chanter equal to him.

A few years later Vasili began to neglect his studies and to roam the city streets, loitering in princely courts, playing foolish pranks with the nobles' sons and the local rabble. Some of his jests were far from playful for when he caught hold of a hand, the arm was wrenched from its socket; when he caught hold of a foot, it dropped off with the leg; and if he caught anyone a clout about the head, that head went spinning away from the shoulders.

Consequently, the men of Novgorod came to the widowed mother, Amalfa Timofeyevna, to register a complaint against this monstrous child of hers.

'Take your son Vasili away from among our children and youngsters; he cripples and kills them with no aim and no object. Children cannot be replaced as cattle can. Remove him, or else we ourselves will deal with him and chase him to the Volkhov River and cast him in its waters.' So Amalfa Timofeyevna waited for the return of her son to upbraid and reprimand him, and to try and make him listen to reason.

'My sweet child,' she implored, 'why do you go about Novgorod making cripples? Your father, at your age, had scarcely a hundred roubles in his pocket, but he did have a brave bodyguard. Look at you, with neither brothers nor guards you will never be able to settle matters with anyone.'

Vasili was displeased with his mother's words, and he stalked off up to his lofty tower. There he decided he would choose a bodyguard. He sat down in his chair and, as fast as he could pen them, wrote little scrolls: 'Whoever would eat, drink and be merry, let him hasten to Vasili's spacious court to partake of a sumptuous feast.' He bound the little scrolls to arrowheads, and shot the arrows into Novgorod. Then Vasili arose and set himself to brewing an intoxicating ale and distilled green wine. He placed casks around the courtyard and, beside each, goblets which held 10 litres. 'Whosoever shall lift in one hand the beaker and drain it at a draught, shall be Vasili's dear friend and faithful companion,' said Vasili.

As the people came out from the cathedrals and churches, they discovered and gathered up the arrows, and those learned in the written word began to read. 'Vasili commands you to a sumptuous feast...' So far they read, but no further, and one and all crowded off to Vasili's.

From his tower, Vasili spied them coming, and thought to himself, 'The ale will never suffice, the green wine will not go round,' and grasping his red club of elmwood he went out before the central gate to the people and spoke the following words: 'Whoever shall raise his cup with one hand, and drain it at a draught; he who can endure my red club of elmwood on his turbulent head – he shall be my chosen friend and brother.'

At this the crowd swayed this way and that, each person hiding behind the other. 'We shall get neither bite nor quaff,' they said, 'only broken limbs to last a lifetime.'

Shortly thereafter a young man came at a run, one Kostya Newtrader, heading for Vasili's courtyard. He drew a cup of wine, quaffed it to the dregs, drew yet another, and drained it too at a draught. Just as the noble youth was about to swallow the third, a mighty blow landed on his head. The draught of wine was arrested in his hand, but he stood firm, and did not move. The black curls on his turbulent head did not stir, the blue kaftan did not slip from his shoulders, the full cup in his hand was not spilled.

'Well, now you have cleared my turbulent head, Vasili,' he cried, 'you must stand me a drink.' Then Vasili took Kostya by his white hands, embraced him warmly, and, conducting him to the guest quarters, sat him down at the oaken board and gave him food and drink. And so it continued, Vasili testing each comer with a mighty blow on the head, until twenty-nine brothers were chosen; the thirtieth, commanding them all, being Vasili himself.

Then Vasili prepared a sumptuous feast for his comrades but did not invite the men of Novgorod. He spoke to his companions: 'Greetings, my brave comrades! We fear no one now in Novgorod.' And news spread through Novgorod of the stout-hearted heroes Vasili had gathered about him: how they held one common hall, and each and all wore coloured raiment.

When they saw that things were going against them, the Novgorodians assembled in secret towers to hold council and to think deep thoughts. Then one of the elders stood forth in their midst, did obeisance to all four sides, stroked his white beard, and, striking the floor with his staff, he said, 'Hail to you, men of Novgorod! We have suffered much at the hands of that reckless youth Vasili, but be not discouraged, my children; let us make an honourable feast, but not invite Vasili to it. He will arrive uninvited and once we have handed him a goblet of wine, he will speak in his cups, and we shall know how far he plots evil against us.'

And all present rose, bowed, and spoke, 'So be it.'

In the early dawn, when the red sun rose, they went out to bid all Novgorod to the feast, only Vasili they did not bid. But when young Vasili heard of the feast they were making, of the kvas and the green wine in preparation, he took with him his brave bodyguard and set off for the feast. They entered the banquet hall, made straight for the hearth-corner, and occupied the most honoured seats. 'Even though you have taken a seat in the great corner,' said the men of Novgorod, 'you are but an unwelcome guest; there is no seat for an unwelcome guest.' Then, as if in mockery, they handed Vasili a goblet of sappy green wine. And the young hot blood raced through Vasili's veins; he grew drunk and merry, and began to boast arrogantly.

'Novgorod is mine,' cried Vasili, 'I will take tithes from her broad lands, take my share of the hares and ducks, take guest-money from the merchant strangers.'

Then all the guests grew drunk and merry, voices rose high, and quarrels fast and furious could be heard. Vasili, more drunk than any, made a great wager that with his brave comrades he would defy all Novgorod. 'If you of Novgorod overcome us, we shall be subject to you. But if it happens we win the day, then for all time you shall be subject to me.' Then with many a handshake and many an unchronicled oath they parted – to meet in deadly combat at the Volkhov bridge on the morrow.

Vasili returned home to his mother, heavy-eyed, drunk and keen to boast of the wager he had laid, staking even his turbulent head that he would go on the morrow with only his bold company of guards to the Volkhov bridge, to defy all Novgorod. When she heard this, his widowed mother wept, and seizing Vasili by his white hands, led him down to the deep vaults, closed the iron doors upon him, and made them fast with bolts. Vasili fell asleep, never to move or waken.

Early the next morning Vasili's brave troops took their stand by the Volkhov River, ready to contend against all Novgorod, and as the spring floods sweep over the meadows, so the men of Novgorod swept up the plain; as the white geese and swans rise up on the Ilmen Lake, so all Novgorod rose against Vasili. Alone, the troop faced the deadly fray and the Novgorodians trampled them underfoot. All their heads were broken, their hands bandaged with kerchiefs, their feet bound up in rushes.

But Vasili's mother had a faithful little maiden, dark of face. She went down to the Volkhov River to fetch water, her buckets swinging like bells over her maple yoke. When she beheld the evil disaster of Vasili's bold youths, she wept bitterly. So, as fast as her feet would carry her, losing her buckets midway, she hastened back to the deep vaults where Vasili slumbered, crying breathlessly, 'Vasili Buslayevich, why do you sleep and not arise? Your brave troops are at their last gasp on the Volkhov bridge.'

Thereupon Vasili wakened, stepped into his boots, flung his fur mantle over one shoulder, donned his cap over one ear and, throwing himself against the bolted doors, smashed the locks and bolts. Not finding his iron mace, Vasili wrenched an iron axle from a cart which stood near, and went running through the wide streets of Novgorod. He reached the bloody scene and saw his brave men knee-deep in gore.

'Hail, brave bodyguard! Not I, the good youth, but my mother betrayed you. Rest now awhile. I shall take turn for each of you.'

And he went in among the men of Novgorod, brandishing his axle. Where he thrust forward a lane appeared, where he drew back a footway; and the Novgorodians lay in heaps. Perceiving that pitiless, inexorable fate was upon them, the Novgorodians filled one cup with yellow gold, another with white silver, and a third with cut gems, and ran to the Kirillov Monastery to offer them to the elderly archbishop, godfather to Vasili.

'Ho, venerable father,' they cried, 'stop your godson, young Vasili Buslayevich, that some may be spared to continue our race.'

Thereupon the venerable elder tore down from the belfry of St Sophia's Cathedral the big bell weighing 3,500 pounds, donned it in place of a cowl, and leaning upon the clapper like a walking-stick, set out for the Volkhov bridge. Straight up to Vasili he strode, calling all the while, 'Stop, godson; hold your slaughter, Vasili. It is not for you to drink the Volkhov dry, nor for you to exterminate all in Novgorod.'

'Ho now, godfather,' called Vasili, 'it is an ill wind that blows hither. The game now is in full swing and here we gamble with heads. And if I gave you no egg on Easter morn, take now this red one on Saint Peter's day.' At this, Vasili smote the bell with his axle, and a groan came from the bell as it split, and the aged arch-bishop sank down on to the moist earth.

Vasili continued to gain on the men of Novgorod and his brave guards picked up courage; their eyes grew bright again, and they chased the men of Novgorod onto the wide plain, to the steep banks of the river, and gave them no chance to turn. So the men of Novgorod sent envoys to Vasili's widowed mother, Amalfa Timo-feyevna, to make intercession for them, saying, 'Remove Vasili and his comrades, that some may yet remain to continue our race.'

The old lady hastened to set out, making her way through the crowded streets. In approaching Vasili, she came not from in front, but crept up behind him, and fell upon his mighty shoulders. 'Hail, son of Buslay,' she cried. 'Cease this slaughter that some be left to continue the race.'

Thereupon Vasili let drop his arms, his white hand released the axle which fell to Moist Mother Earth, and he said, 'Indeed, my fair lady mother. You have exercised cunning to have taken me thus unawares, otherwise in my fury I might have slain you in place of a Novgorodian. But now I shall obey you, for so is it the will of God.'

And Vasili took her by her white hands, and went back home to the palace of white stone.

Sadko the Rich Merchant

In famous Novgorod dwelt merchant Sadko, the Rich Guest. To begin with Sadko possessed no golden treasure, only his well-tuned zither. He went about playing at feasts and his zither made all merry. But it chanced that on a certain day, Sadko was bidden to no feast; neither was he on the next day, nor the one after that. In great sorrow he went to Lake Ilmen, sat himself down on Moist

Mother Earth, and there began to play upon his well-tuned zither. The waves ran high on the lake and Sadko, full of fear, departed in haste and returned to his beloved Novgorod.

Another day went by, but Sadko was bidden to no worshipful feast. Another came and went – still he was unbidden. On the third day – the same thing. In great sorrow he went again to Lake Ilmen, sat down on Moist Mother Earth and played upon his well-tuned zither. Then the waters rose high on Ilmen Lake, and from the waves emerged Tsar Morskoy,[1] the ocean king.

'I know not how to reward you, Sadko of Novgorod, for your entertainment, for your skilful playing,' he said. 'Perhaps with golden treasure? Go, now, back to Novgorod, and lay a great wager. Stake your turbulent head, try to convince the townsfolk that in Ilmen Lake you know there are fish with golden fins. Then, Sadko, you will make your fortune.'

Sadko return to his beloved Novgorod and there, at last, he was bidden to a worshipful feast. He played on his well-tuned zither, and he was served with food and drink. Sadko began to brag: 'Hear one and all, you merchants of Novgorod! I know of a wonder of wonders. In Ilmen Lake are fish with fins of gold. I stake my turbulent head – more than that I have not. On what will you stake the wager with me? Will you stake your booths of precious merchandise?'

Three merchants came forward and poured scorn upon him.

'You are a fool!' they said. 'We will stake our three booths of precious wares that there is no such thing.'

'Go, then,' instructed Sadko. 'Bind a silken net, go down to the lake and cast the net three times into the water.'

The first casting produced a little fish with fins of gold; the second, another little fish with fins of gold; and at the final casting, yet another golden-finned fish.

Sadko received the three booths of precious wares, joined the

1. Tsar Morskoy is another name for Tsar Mora, the sea god (see *Dazhbog and Lara*, p29).

guild of merchants and began to trade and make a great profit. He took a wife and built a beautiful mansion of white stone where the ceilings of the chambers were painted to resemble the heavens, with the sun, moon and stars shining down. Soon he possessed a fleet of thirty ships and he became known as 'Sadko, the Rich Merchant of Novgorod'.

Then Sadko the Merchant held a worshipful feast and invited the people of glorious Novgorod, as well as the elders Foma Nazarev and Luka Zinoviev. Each and all ate and drank his fill, one and all were loud in praise and boasting. The elders asked him: 'Sadko, why do you never brag or boast?'

Sadko cried out, 'What shall I, Sadko the Merchant, brag or boast about? My inexhaustible golden treasure? My coloured garments too numerous for me to wear out? My brave and incorruptible bodyguards? But stay, let me boast of my treasure, because it can buy up all the wares of Novgorod, good, bad and indifferent, so that none shall remain in the city.' Scarcely had Sadko spoken when the two elders sprang to their nimble feet, took thirty thousand roubles from the treasury, and staked a great wager against Sadko that he could not buy up all the wares, good, bad and indifferent, and leave none for sale in Novgorod.

The next morning, bright and early, Sadko roused his brave bodyguards, dealt out golden treasure without measure, and sent them to the markets. He himself went to the grand bazaar to buy up all the wares, good, bad and indifferent. On the following morning, Sadko again rose early, wakened his bodyguards, distributed treasure to them without measure and sent them forth to the markets. He himself went to the grand bazaar and found wares there, far more than before! To the glory of Novgorod the wares had doubled. But again Sadko bought everything up, good, bad and indifferent, with his treasure. Also on the third day, Sadko rose very early, roused his bodyguards, dealt out treasure to them, and sent them out into the busy streets. He himself went to the markets and to the grand bazaar. To his astonishment he discovered that the stocks had trebled; were piled up threefold. Such was the glory of Novgorod.

Then Sadko thought deeply. 'What possessed me to buy up all the goods the wide world produces? Even if I were to purchase all the wares of Moscow, still more will flow in from over the seas. Sadko is powerful, but Novgorod is more powerful still.' Then he yielded the great wager and gave up the thirty thousand roubles.

But Sadko still had a problem: he had bought an immense stock of wares, good bad and indifferent, and did not know what to do with them. So he decided to embark upon a trading voyage to rid himself of his new and immense stock.

He loaded his thirty ships with the wares of Novgorod and sailed away down the Volkhov River to Lake Ladoga, thence into the Neva River, and on through the blue sea to distant Constantinople, the queen of cities. There he sold the merchandise of Novgorod and made a great profit. He filled many casks with yellow gold, white silver and precious gems, and each cask held forty buckets. Then he turned to sail back again over the open blue sea to Novgorod. But the good ships came to a halt on the sea. They never moved forward despite the fact that the waves dashed up high and the winds blew into the dark red sails.

Sadko understood what was the matter. 'It is clear that Tsar Morskoy is angry with us. For all the years we have been sailing over the blue sea, not once have we paid tribute to the ocean king. Now he demands a tribute to be sent down in the deep blue sea.'

His brave guards brought out a cask of silver and let it down into the blue sea depths. The waves crashed against the vessels, the sails were shredded, the ships strained, but not one of them stirred on the blue sea. Then the men took a cask of yellow gold and lowered it into the blue sea. Again the waves pounded, the sails flapped, the ships strained, but still they remained motionless.

With deep sorrow Sadko spoke once again: 'It is now plain to me that Tsar Morskoy demands a living man from among us down in the blue sea. You must, therefore, make ingots of lead, upon which each is to inscribe his name. As for me, I shall inscribe mine on a gold nugget. The man whose lot sinks to the bottom of the sea shall be sacrificed to Tsar Morskoy.'

The sailors did as they were instructed and made ingots of lead, and a gold nugget for Sadko. Each one carved his name, and they let down the lots into the blue sea. To his dismay, Sadko saw that the leaden ingots floated like bark upon the waves, while his gold nugget plunged straight down to the bottom of the sea.

Now Sadko was a man of great cunning but little courage. He tried desperately to change his fate, and called to his men: 'There has been a serious mistake! The lots were not true. Make for yourselves ingots of gold and I shall have a nugget of lead.'

This time the guards made up ingots of gold and signed their names on them, while Sadko signed the leaden nugget; then the lots were let down into the blue sea. But the same thing happened: the golden lots swam like ducks on water while only the lot of Sadko sank to the floor of the sea.

Thereupon Sadko spoke once more: 'Ho, brothers, brave troops. It is obvious that the sea king has summoned Sadko the Merchant himself down in the blue sea. Bring me now my carved inkhorn, my swan quill pen, the paper with my coat-of-arms.'

And Sadko began to sign away his worldly possessions. He bequeathed a large amount to God's churches, another to the poor, another to his brethren, a sum to his wife, and what remained to his comrades. When he had finished he began to weep, and gave his final instructions: 'Hand me my well-tuned zither, that in these last moments I may strum it one more time. And throw me a plank of oakwood on the waters so that I shall not be so fearful to meet death.'

His brave bodyguard let down the plank of oak, and Sadko, holding his zither, left the ship. He bade farewell to Mother Earth, to glorious Novgorod and to his loyal men. As soon as he stepped onto the wooden plank the ships sped forward like a flight of black ravens, leaving him alone.

Sadko floated on the blue sea waves, exhausted and terrified; then he fell asleep. When he awoke he found himself on the very bed of the ocean depths. Up through the waves he could see the red sun burning. Close by stood a white stone palace where the ocean king was sitting upon his throne. Addressing Sadko, he said: 'I have sent for you that you may tell me which is now of greater value in Russia: gold or silver or damascened steel? For the empress has disputed with me on this matter.'

'Gold and silver are indeed precious in Russia,' replied Sadko, 'but steel no less. For without gold and silver a man may live; but without steel or iron he cannot.'

The king addressed him again: 'Ho, merchant Sadko! For many years you have sailed the seas but offered no tribute to the lord of the ocean. Now you have come as a gift to me. Since you play the zither like an expert, play for me now here in the deep sea.'

Then Sadko began to play, and as he played Tsar Morskoy got up to dance. How he danced down in the deep blue sea! Sadko played all that day and yet another, even a third day he played, and all the while the sea king danced. The blue sea rose, the waters churned with sand, a terrible storm broke out and great waves appeared. Boats were wrecked, merchandise spoiled and many people drowned. Good Christian folk began to pray to Saint Nikolai of Mozhaisk, the protector of seafarers.

Suddenly, Sadko heard a voice from behind his right shoulder. 'Sadko of Novgorod, cease your playing at once.'

'I cannot, for fear of the ocean king who has cast a spell on me,' answered Sadko, turning around to the white-haired man who stood there. 'I must obey him.'

'Then,' said the old man, 'you must snap the strings of your zither and break its pegs. When the tsar sees that it is impossible for you to go on playing he will try another way of keeping you in his power. Perhaps he will offer you a beautiful damsel in marriage. If so you must obey, for you are in his kingdom. In the morning you will be asked to rise early and choose the maiden who pleases you most. However, you must not choose any maiden of the first one hundred who go past, nor any from the second hundred, but only the last of the third hundred. This will be the black-haired nymph Chernava. She is the one you must take as your bride. But beware! You must not remain with her on your wedding night, neither must you embrace her, otherwise you will stay in the sea forever. If, however, you follow my instructions everything will turn out well for you and you shall once more return to Novgorod. When you return to Holy Russia you must promise to build a church in honour of Saint Nikolai of Mozhaisk, for I am he.' With that the old man vanished from sight.

Sadko followed his instructions to the letter. He snapped the strings of his zither and broke the pegs. Tsar Morskoy cried, 'Ho, young Sadko, why have you stopped playing?'

'My strings have snapped and the keys are useless.'

The tsar then asked, as predicted, 'Would you not like to wed here in the deep sea?'

'Your will is my command, for you are the lord of the sea world and I have but to obey.'

Then said Tsar Morskoy: 'Rise early, Sadko, and choose the most beautiful maiden.' So Sadko rose early, and let the first one hundred maidens pass; also the second, and likewise the third, except for the very last, fair Chernava the nymph, whom he chose.

The tsar ordered a great banquet and afterwards the couple retired to their chamber. Sadko did not embrace his wife but fell instead into a deep sleep. When he awoke, he found himself on the steep banks of the River Chernava and beyond, sailing down the Volkhov River into Novgorod, was his fleet of ships.

Here was Sadko's young wife thinking that he and his troop were out in the blue sea! Here were Sadko's brave men thinking that he was forever lost in the ocean depths. But there stood Sadko himself on the steep river bank. After greeting his comrades fondly he conducted them to his white stone mansion. There his young wife rejoiced and embraced him, and later they unloaded all the rich cargo on his ships.

With his enormous riches Sadko built a cathedral to honour Saint Nikolai of Mozhaisk and another to Saints Boris and Gleb. He sailed no more upon the blue sea but dwelt happily at home in Novgorod.

The Religious Calendar
of the Ancient Eastern Slavs

Ancient Holiday	Deity	Christian Feast
Winter Solstice	Rod	Christmas and Theophany
Spring Equinox	Volos	Annunciation
2 May (day of germination)		Canonization of Saints Boris and Gleb
4 June	Iarilo	Ascension
Summer Solstice	Simargl	Trinity
24 June	Kupalo	St John the Baptist
24 July–7 August (beginning and end of harvest)		Martyrdom of Saints Boris and Gleb; Transfiguration
9 September	Rozhanitsy	Nativity of the Mother of God
28 October	Mokosh	St Paraskeva

Sources for Further Reading

As an anthology for the general reader, this book does not carry specific bibliographical citations. I have, of course, consulted secondary literature for the Foreword and for the short prefaces to some of the narratives. As to the tales themselves, I have made use of texts both in Russian and in English, rearranging, modifying or adding to the material to the degree that it suited my purposes. The publications cited below have been indispensable, in one way or another, for the outcome of this work.

A. N. Afanas'ev, *Narodnye russkie skazki i legendi*, 2 vols, Berlin, 1922

G. Alexinsky, 'Slavonic Mythology', *New Larousse Encyclopedia of Mythology*, London and New York, 1959

N. K. Chadwick, *Russian Heroic Poetry*, Cambridge, 1932

S. H. Cross and O. P. Sherbowitz-Wetzor, *The Russian Primary Chronicle*, Cambridge, Massachusetts, 1973

J. Curtin, *Myths and Folk Tales of the Russians, Western Slavs and Magyars*, Boston, 1890

G. P. Fedotov, *The Russian Religious Mind*, Vol. 1, *Kievan Christianity: The Tenth to the Thirteenth Centuries*, New York, 1960

C. Fillingham Coxwell, *Siberian and Other Folk-Tales*, London, 1925

A. F. Gilferding, *Oneszhskia byliny zapisannia A.F. Gilferdingom*, 3 vols, Saint Petersburg, 1894

M. Gimbutas, 'Ancient Slavic Religion: A Synopsis', *To Honour Roman Jakobson: Essays on the Occasion of his Seventieth Birthday*, Vol. 1, The Hague and Paris, 1967, pp. 738–59

N. Guterman, *Russian Fairy Tales*, London, n.d.

I. F. Hapgood, *The Epic Songs of Russia*, New York, 1885

J. Hubbs, *Mother Russia*, Indiana, 1988

L. J. Ivanits, *Russian Folk Belief*, New York, 1989

R. Jakobson, 'Slavic Mythology', *Funk and Wagnall's Standard Dictionary of Folklore, Mythology and Legend*, Vol. 2, New York 1949–50, pp.1025–8

F. J. Oinas, *Essays on Russian Folklore and Mythology*, Columbus, 1985

W. Ralston, *Songs of the Russian People*, London, 1872

B. A. Rybakov, 'Kalendar IV v. iz zemli polian', *Sovetskaia arkheleologiia*, no.4, 1962, pp. 66–89

I. Sakharov, *Skazaniia russkogo naroda*, 2 vols, Saint Petersburg, 1841

F. Sciacca, 'Royal Farmers: A Folkloric Investigation into the Pagan Origins of the Cult of Boris and Gleb', *Ulbandus Review*, I, I, 1977, 3–14

B. Sokolov, *Russkiy fol'klor*, Vols.1–2, Moscow, 1929–30

E. Warner, *Heroes, Monsters and Other Worlds from Russian Mythology*, London, 1985

S. A. Zenkovsky, *Medieval Russia's Epics, Chronicles and Tales*, New York, 1974